Dr. Keesha is passionate about autoimmune dysfunction becau; has discovered the path to healing with nutrient-dense food. cook delicious meals that move you towards optimal health and vitality. Her information and recipes help you change the way you look at food, both when you're cooking at home for our families, and when we're eating out and traveling.

Dr. Mariza Snyder, Author of the *Smart Mom's Guide to Essential Oils* and *The DASH Diet Cookbook*

Anything that Dr. Keesha does is heart-centered and thoughtfully prepared. This book is no exception. She always tries to meet people where they are. She loves to work with people, teach and share her vast wellness knowledge. This book is a true testament to her passion for holistic health. She inspires and motivates readers on how simple, accessible recipes can bring food and meal preparation back into their kitchens. This book should be in everyone's kitchen!

Kerry McClure, Co-Author of *Beyond Meditation: Making Mindfulness Accessible for Everyone* and *Gratitude: A Mindful Pause*

It is hard to categorize this incredible gift of wisdom and knowledge as only a cookbook. In the true spirit of "teach a man to fish," Dr. Keesha has offered so much more than recipes. She helps the reader to understand more about themselves so that they can put to use the correct nutritional choices for their body, mind, and spirit. Couple this with an assortment of delicious, nourishing recipes, and "The Autoimmune Cookbook" becomes a one-stop toolkit for healing and thriving.

Dr. Sarica Cernohous, L.Ac., Author of *The Funky Kitchen: Easy Techniques from Our Ancestors for Improved Digestion, Enhanced Vitality and Joy!*

As a doctor and busy mom living with autoimmune disease, I appreciate having a recipe resource that makes meal time quick, easy, and delicious! Dr. Keesha's recipes are so simple and nourishing that they make feeding my family the easiest part of my day!

Dr. Jolene Brighten, Women's Hormone Expert and Leading Authority on Post-Birth Control Syndrome

Dr. Keesha has solved the mystery on how to eat a nourishing healthy diet without it being complicated or taking too much time. This recipe book is full of quick, easy and tasty recipes with variations to keep things exciting. But don't make the mistake of thinking you will only be getting recipes. This book is a comprehensive resource explaining the underlying root causes of autoimmunity. It takes a closer look into the role that food, genetics, toxins, leaky gut and trauma play in the diagnosis of autoimmune conditions and gives the reader the important, and often under discussed, truths about gaining freedom and restoring health and vitality.

Shanna Lee, Frequency Alchemist, Personal Coach

We rarely eat just to survive. For most of us, our relationship with food provides love, nurturing, medicine, emotional protection and sometimes, self-abuse. Which is why Dr. Keesha's book is so groundbreaking: she makes a solid case for why the foods we eat, and why we eat them, determine our quality of life and our physical, emotional and spiritual wellbeing. This is so much more than a cookbook, it is an unprecedented guide for true health.

Tricia Nelson, Emotional Eating Expert and
Founder of www.HealYourHunger.com

I thought this would be a traditional cookbook, but I was delighted to find that it's so much more! In addition to the fabulous, easy to fix recipes, Dr. Keesha takes you on a step-by-step journey to understand the role food, chemicals, stress and our environment play in our health and exactly what to do about it. This new cook book will give you back your power to live with vitality!

Katana Abbott, CFP®, CSA

The Quick and Easy Autoimmune Paleo Cookbook is exactly what busy moms like me need! It only includes ingredients that I know supports my family's health (and don't trigger reactions like rashes, temper-tantrums and tummy troubles). Gluten free, sugar free, and tons of dairy free options, to easily and deliciously feed your family without feeding inflammation and autoimmunity.

Sounds amazing, right? It IS!

With just 7 kinds of ingredients, simple to follow recipes and easy "make it yours" suggestions, I can whip up the perfect nourishing meal, snack, or dessert in no time with no stress.

Dr. Keesha's Quick and Easy Autoimmune Paleo Cookbook is special because she includes everything about where autoimmune disease comes from, what makes it worse, and exactly how to heal it - in straightforward, easy-to understand language that's totally actionable and fun to read. I love that I can sit down to "pick out a recipe" and dive into my favorite topic . . . how to create vibrant health!

When I'm feeling great I do great things for my family . . . like cook them the scrumptious meals in The Quick and Easy Autoimmune Paleo Cookbook!

Elissa Arnheim, certified fermentationist and health coach

"I am so excited Dr. Keesha created this much needed cookbook! As a busy mom, health coach, and an autoimmune disease survivor, I know how hard it is to plan meals that are easy to make and don't take hours of preparation. Dr. Keesha's cookbook is packed with tons of educational information and amazing recipes the whole family will love!"

Jaime Ward, Functional & Integrative Nutrition Health Coach

The Quick & Easy
Autoimmune Paleo Cookbook

Anti-Inflammatory Recipes with 7 Ingredients or Less for Busy People

Dr. Keesha Ewers

samadhi
press

samadhi
p r e s s

The Quick & Easy Autoimmune Paleo Cookbook: Anti-Inflammatory Recipes with 7 Ingredients or Less for Busy People

Library of Congress Control Number: 2018942908

First Printing: June 2018
ISBN: 978-0-9988771-2-9
Printed in USA
Samadhi Press

Book Cover Design by Debbie O'Byrne
Photos by Ken & Tania Shepard, Azzura Photography

Dr. Keesha Ewers
22525 SE 64th Pl.
Suite 2280
Issaquah, WA 98027
(425) 391-3376
info@DrKeesha.com
www.DrKeesha.com

Ordering Information
Special discounts available on quantity purchases by corporations, associations, educators, and others. For details, contact publisher as above.

Booking, Press & Speaking Inquiries
Dr. Keesha Ewers, PhD, ARNP, LLC, is an engaging and popular speaker at professional associations, Harvard, on television and radio, and from the TEDx stage. She speaks on a wide range of topics, from natural healing of autoimmune diseases and cancer, to epigenetics, to restoring healthy libido. To learn more, see her speaker's page at www.drkeesha.com/speaking/.

This book is not intended as a substitute for the medical advice of physicians. The reader should regularly consult a physician in matters relating to his/her health and particularly with respect to any symptoms that may require diagnosis or medical attention.

Autoimmune disease is by definition a mind and body at war with itself.
When you are at war with yourself, there can be no winner.
Are you ready for a ceasefire?

Dedication

To all who suffer from pain, be it physical, mental, emotional or spiritual.
May this book be instrumental in bringing you peace.

Other books by Dr. Keesha Ewers

*Solving the Autoimmune Puzzle: The Woman's Guide to
Reclaiming Emotional Freedom and Vibrant Health*

The Mystic Medicine Mandala Adult Coloring Book

Table of Contents

Section 5: Autoimmune Recipes for Busy People

Introduction

Healthy citizens are the greatest asset any country can have."

—Winston Churchill

I am one of the 50 million Americans who has received an autoimmune diagnosis. I know what it's like to watch with dismay as my menu options dwindle and my environmental resilience disappears. I know what happens when it seems your body has betrayed you. You can become depressed, you might reach for convenience foods that you think will provide comfort, only to find that a minute on the lips leads to pain in the hips. If it hurts to move, you will stop moving. Then you might start gaining weight, becoming even more discouraged and even ashamed that you can't get a handle on your life. You might start going online to find a quick-fix diet solution. You may be too overwhelmed with fatigue to follow an eating plan that would help you, and opt instead for convenience foods that you know are not doing you any good.

Then there's the frustration that arises when you *are* eating and doing "everything right" and yet you *still* don't feel good. You might believe that your body has betrayed you and resent the hell out of it. You begin to think of your body as your adversary and of food as the enemy since you feel so terrible after every meal. You say words like, "I am struggling with my _____". Fill in the blank. It could be your weight, your energy level, your libido, your sleep, your skin, your mood, your menstrual cycle, your digestion, your fertility if you are trying to conceive. You keep "fighting" against pain, brain fog, puffiness, and food cravings.

This is the trap I found myself in twenty-five years ago. I found a way out and wrote a book called *Solving the Autoimmune Puzzle: The Woman's Guide to Reclaiming Emotional Freedom and Vibrant Health* for people to use as a roadmap find their way out of suffering. I went into depth with information about how to reverse inflammation and autoimmune disease but did not go into depth with a food plan or recipes for changing your diet. I have written the book you are reading now to fill that gap.

The road back from autoimmunity is not straight or without bumps and pot holes. The reason is that you are a unique puzzle, different from every other person on this planet. I am going to teach you a method for understanding and solving your unique health puzzle. I am not going to fix you. I am going to provide the information you need for how to eat to reverse your own autoimmunity. However, food is only one piece of the inflammation puzzle.

What causes inflammation? It is the body's attempt to protect and defend itself after exposure to a potential threat such as viruses and bacteria; or to repair itself after an injury. The inflammatory response is an emergency signal, or feedback mechanism, that alerts your body's immune system to come and repair the damage. This is not necessarily "bad," but it is not a sustainable state for your body to remain in for prolonged periods. In other words, the acute inflammatory response of redness, pain, and swelling as a result of a cut on your finger is necessary to prevent an infection. After the white blood cells rush to the injured area and ingest the damaged cells or microbes, the inflammatory response recedes, and healing completes.

Conversely, chronic or systemic inflammation can go undetected in the body until you receive the diagnosis of an autoimmune disease, heart disease, or even cancer. Chronic inflammation is caused by lifestyle choices such as diet, excess body weight, stress, poor dental health, smoking, alcohol consumption, and a lack of exercise. Environmental triggers such as pollution, mold, dust, chemicals, and food allergies and sensitivities can also cause inflammation.

If you fail to eliminate the root cause of your inflammation or continue to repeatedly exposure yourself to the offending trigger, you will create what I call a "hypervigilant" immune system. When your immune system becomes trigger-happy, it can even start perceiving and tagging the foods you eat as foreign invaders. Living with a hypervigilant immune system is like living with an angry, trigger-happy gunslinger from the old west, who shoots first and walks away without bothering to ask any questions. Your list of perceived threats can go from one or two mildly reactive foods or environmental sensitivities to an ever-growing list of reactive agents, until you feel like the girl or boy in a bubble who is living with an ever-shrinking list of foods and life experiences you can tolerate. This is obviously not a great life.

There is no quick fix to ending inflammation or autoimmune disease. If you have been exhausted, feeling sick for many years, and are even on multiple medications, you will need to be patient. Once you begin implementing the tools you will learn in this book, you will likely start feeling better soon, but ending your autoimmunity can take a while. It requires patience and perseverance. I often observe women having far more patience and perseverance with others than they have for themselves. That is something we are going to work on together. You are worth persevering for, you deserve loving self-care, you are worthy of nourishment on all levels. Your body deserves the best nutritional plan you can give it. Junk food is not a reward; it is a punishment, and I want to help you make that shift in perception, because the part of you who is in pain desperately needs you to love her (or him).

Please also keep in mind that if you already have an autoimmune disease, potentially with organ damage, it might have taken 10, 20, or even 30 years to develop. This is for certain; it did not happen "all of a sudden" or "overnight" the way most of us believe when we are diagnosed. That said, it won't take decades for you to start feeling better, because I am giving you a quick-start program that will get you on the right track as you learn to solve your own health puzzle. I am teaching you the method I used to reverse my own autoimmune disease within six months of diagnosis and have now successfully used to end inflammation and autoimmunity for hundreds of my patients.

What You Can Expect

As you learn and implement the method I am laying out for you, your symptoms of fatigue, pain, digestive problems, insomnia, anger, depression, anxiety, and inflammation will start to reduce within 7-10 days. You will start to see a change in your weight as you start to lose puffiness and swelling (signs of inflammation) over the next 10-21 days. To make the math easier, expect a 50% reduction of symptoms over the next few weeks, provided you take the steps I describe. You will get out of this what you put into it.

It will take time for you to create and integrate new habits. You *must* schedule this time for yourself. I find that women with autoimmunity are often perfectionists who struggle with self-care, focusing instead on caring for others. We are all busy people living in a productivity-oriented society. Time is one of the most valuable commodities we have. Most of my patients tell me they simply do not have the time to spend in the kitchen cooking whole foods from scratch that will enliven their cells. I get it. I am also very busy. I don't spend a lot of time in the kitchen any longer. In fact, I have learned to feed myself nutritiously

and efficiently. These two concepts are not mutually exclusive.

This cookbook was created with the busy person in mind. The recipes are easy and fast to make. Most of them have seven ingredient categories or less. I have created what I call master recipe templates for you. You can make them very simple with seven ingredients or less or you can be adventurous and make them more complex. Some of them, such as the cake, take more time and can include more ingredients, depending on how fancy you want to get. I included the cake recipe here because sometimes you might want to create something special for someone special on a special day. However, rest assured, you can feed yourself on seven ingredients or less easily and in little time with the recipes in this book. I know, because this is how I eat.

The Method

This is not the Standard American Diet (SAD) from the Standard American Medical (Uncle SAM) model of healthcare you are used to that focuses on the old food pyramid or matching symptoms to drugs. Uncle SAM's healthcare model is great for acute emergencies. If you are having a heart attack, need to have a broken bone set, or urgently need your appendix out, please call Uncle SAM. But the Uncle SAM model is sorely lacking when it comes to preventing disease or ending autoimmune disease, which is what we are up to in this cookbook. Learning to break free of the food pyramid is true preventative medicine.

My patients and integrative medicine health coach students often get confused about which foods are "good" and which foods are "bad." I am going to say right here that there is no good or bad food.

However, most of what is on grocery store shelves today did not exist 100 years ago. In other words, most of it isn't even food at all. Additionally, most of us have leaky gut now. (We'll take a much closer look at this in Chapter Three.) Suffice to say for now, our immune systems are more reactive, or hypervigilant, today than the immune systems of people 100 years ago.

This book is meant to give you a structure to begin your journey to a healthier digestive and immune system. It's the companion book to *Solving the Autoimmune Puzzle: The Woman's Guide to Reclaiming Emotional Freedom and Vibrant Health*. Many of the concepts and ideas you will be introduced to in this book are written about in more depth in *Solving the Autoimmune Puzzle*. In this book, I focus on food, which is where I start with all of my patients. But we are not going to be limited to just food you put into your mouth. I am also going to be talking about mental and emotional and spiritual nutrition.

Are you like my patients and students when they first start out on this journey? Are you like I was when I was first diagnosed with autoimmune disease? Are you one of the confused? Don't know what diet is right for you? Have you read all about super foods and followed dietary programs that have promised results you didn't get? You are not alone. That's why I call this a puzzle. For now, let's start with the foundation that food is medicine, love is medicine, and self-care is medicine. You are going to be learning to care for yourself in the way your body has been requesting, perhaps for years, but likely you have not known how to listen and respond to it. So, let's get started and begin solving your food puzzle.

I am going to share my own story in the next chapter. If you have already heard me speak or have read *Solving the Autoimmune Puzzle*, you can skip ahead to Chapter Two.

Understanding Autoimmunity

CHAPTER ONE

My Personal Autoimmune Puzzle

"Each patient carries his own doctor inside him."

—Norman Cousins

When I was in my early 30s, I was diagnosed with rheumatoid arthritis (RA). RA is an autoimmune disease that is considered incurable. One day I was running marathons, working part time as a registered nurse in my local hospital, raising my four beautiful children, and preparing to take a family vacation to Florida. The next day I was aching with pain, could hardly move, and some of my joints were swollen and red. I went to see my doctor. After blood tests and x-rays, I was informed I had Rheumatoid Arthritis (RA). How, I wondered, did "all of a sudden" I develop RA when I exercised, ate home-cooked meals, and was healthy when compared to lots of people in my community? I have since heard many of my patients ask me the same question.

I was offered a cancer-fighting drug and some strong anti-inflammatory drugs as "treatment." Since my grandfather had also had RA, my doctor told me it was likely genetic and shrugged her shoulders saying there was not much else to be discussed. I asked her if my diet had any impact on my genetics and inflammation. Was there something I could do besides take the drugs? She responded with a firm and very dismissive "no."

I went home and threw myself into research articles about RA on my computer. I was determined to solve this puzzle quickly. My first and foremost concern was my family. How would my children fare if I was in constant pain? I was beset with anxiety on their behalf. I turned to a familiar refuge. I baked my favorite "comfort" food—chocolate chip cookies—to sustain me during what was turning out to be hours of reading research articles.

I had to stop my daily jogging because of my painful joints. I noticed my mood becoming jagged as irritability floated to the surface due to my lack of exercise. Running had been my one and only free time away from the responsibilities of child rearing. Deprived of my morning run, I was getting snappy and short tempered. I also felt impatient with the pain I was in. This was not my normal state of being. I was used to being called "the Energizer Bunny" and having endless energy. Now I was just exhausted. With my energy went my libido—both gone as the pain settled in. My self-image and self-worth were being affected—not by RA, but by the way I was responding to it.

I began gaining weight. I had never been thin as a child or as a teen. I had what I called a "normal" body type and had to exercise regularly to keep it that way. With my emotional distress, I started baking more of the foods I and my family loved. If my kids couldn't have a "fun and active mom" they could have a mom that kept them well fed and happy with their favorite foods. Those foods were of course baked goods with plenty of sugar, chocolate, milk, and flour in them.

Eventually, in my frantic research, I found an article about yoga as an "alternative treatment" for autoimmunity. As I munched an oatmeal chocolate chip cookie and drank a glass of milk to wash it down, I decided to go to my first yoga class. During class the teacher mentioned the word *Ayurveda*.

Ayurveda, he said, was the sister science of Yoga. It came from India and was a way of individualizing our daily routine. We all have different body types, and we all require different diets, sleep schedules, exercise programs, and learning methods. For me, this was revolutionary. I was a nurse, completely steeped in Western medicine. I had never considered anything beyond the food pyramid and the American Heart Association or the American Diabetic Association guidelines for food plans.

I went home and straight away got on the computer to research Ayurveda. I was filled with excitement, elation, and hope as I spent the next two hours reading about this 10,000-year-old science of living

according to your unique constitutional type. I learned that these body types are called doshas. There are 3 constitutional types and they are known as vata, pitta, and kapha. I began studying up on my particular body type.

I soon discovered *why* I had RA. This had not been a question I had explored beyond "why me," "why now" victimization. It struck me that the *why* was the most important factor in getting to an actual cure rather than just "managing symptoms." I discovered that my inflammation was being aggravated by so many of my daily habits. Not only my daily routine, but the way I thought and the way I held onto frustration and anger. I was not digesting my feelings or past experiences properly.

Autoimmunity, from an Ayurvedic perspective, is undigested anger. I was not friends with the woman I saw in the mirror each day. Internally I was a war zone. I had an adversarial relationship with my body. I had spent most of my adult life trying to "beat it into shape" by literally pounding away over miles and miles of asphalt with my running shoes. I had starved it, hated it, berated it. I had even allowed others to cut out parts that I saw as responsible for causing me pain, such as my tonsils, varicose veins, and gall bladder.

This idea of inflammation and pain stemming from my food choices and my thoughts was new. This was revolutionary. This was mind blowing. Ayurveda was a whole new paradigm for me. I had to sit with it and process it. I took a meditation class and began meditating daily.

Death by Suicide

One day, as I was meditating, the word "autoimmune" entered my mind. As I sat, I began to think of it from different perspectives. The word *auto-immune*, I realized, meant I was attacking myself. I began self-inquiry along this line. Why was I attacking me? Why was I killing myself? My immune system was attacking me as if I were a virus or bacteria. Why was I not friends with myself? Asking the question "why" was the second piece of the puzzle that got me closer to understanding my health dilemma.

That day during meditation and self-inquiry, I followed the why question as if I was retracing my steps back through a labyrinth I had gotten lost in. I visualized a golden thread going back to my childhood and tried to find where it started. When did I decide to attack myself? When did I start viewing myself as a virus or bacteria that needed to be done away with?

Another Piece of the Puzzle Revealed

That thought thread led me back to being ten years old. I was a Navy brat and that meant I moved a lot. In fact, by the time I was fourteen, I had moved twenty-one times. I was extremely introverted and painfully shy. Then, when I was in fourth grade, I started getting called into one of the administrator's offices.

I thought I was in trouble when my name was called out over the intercom in my class to go to the office. I was embarrassed and scared. What had I done? I had never been called into a school office and was known in my other schools and at home as being a "good and well-behaved girl." The first few times I was called to this administrator's office, he just talked to me about behaving in class. I stammered that I was behaving and he let me return to class.

Nonetheless, whenever the intercom rang in the classroom, I felt my heart race and my breathing grow shallow and fast. My hands got clammy as I clutched the number 2 pencil, and the green lines on the tan sheet of paper began to blur.

The Monster in the Shadow

As you may have guessed, these visits to the office turned into something other than talk. He began sexually abusing me and telling me that if I wasn't good, I would be back "for more." I began experiencing headaches and stomach pain every morning when I woke up. I didn't want to go to school anymore. This was unusual because in spite of my shyness, I was an insatiable reader and learner and absolutely loved school. I had always been a good student with no prior attempts at ditching school. I started gaining weight and using sugar as comfort food. My mom was a great baker and we usually had some form of homemade treat cooling on the counter top in the kitchen after school. These gluten- and sugar-filled treats became my solace.

Heeding the Call

Flash forward to my 30s during my meditation, sitting on my cushion. My eyes flew open as the realization hit me squarely between the eyes. At ten years old, I had decided that death was the only way out of a terrible situation. This conclusion had been recorded in my cells and then impacted my genetic expression. It had activated my family history of RA.

As I began to implement a new lifestyle, I soon discovered there were several other pieces to this puzzle. I had been exposed to second-hand cigarette smoke in my childhood. I was treated for frequent urinary tract infections with antibiotics early in my life. I was also prescribed antibiotics multiple times in my adolescent years to treat cases of strep throat. I was addicted to sugar and ate it disguised as "healthy" homemade treats, which also contained gluten and dairy, both of which (I later discovered through functional medicine testing) I am quite intolerant to. I used over-the-counter Ibuprofen frequently to get me through my marathon training and running schedule.

Then there was the emotional and psychological side. I was a perfectionist and drove myself hard throughout my early teen and adult years. I was also a harsh judge of myself and others and did not forgive readily. I held onto the hurts of the past, erroneously thinking that keeping them close would protect me from being hurt again.

But the missing piece to this puzzle, the one that reversed my autoimmune disease for good, was the realization that I believed I was not worth protecting, I was not safe, and I was not loveable unless I was perfect. I had what I now call an "autoimmune mindset." This is a state of such overwhelm, such busyness, such striving for improvement, that the body has to scream to get your attention.

I had early warnings, soft whispers from my body. I had acne in my teens that I took Accutane for. I got extremely nauseated when I went on the oral contraceptive pill. I struggled with my weight. I had terrible brain fog. My knees began to ache. My moods went crazy before I started my periods. I craved sugar every afternoon. I woke up tired every morning and fought

to get out of bed. Each and every one of these issues are part of the same root cause, and all of them were warning signs from my body that things were imbalanced and getting worse.

Like many of my patients, I took a pill for every ill to manage my symptoms. This did not solve the root issue, it just made my body have to turn up the volume. When did I finally pay attention? When my pain was so great I couldn't move. When my joints were angry and red and inflamed. My puzzle was starting to take shape and I was finally ready to look at the pieces and the whole picture. I was miserable and motivated to find some answers.

Within one year of implementing the method I am laying out for you here, my RA was reversed. It has now been over twenty years since I have had any sign of my autoimmune disease. This is not the normal trajectory of RA in the Western medicine paradigm. In fact, as my doctor had told me, it's considered incurable.

Healing the Whole Person
I knew the reversal of my disease was so dramatic because I had been willing to explore my mental health, emotional health, physical health, and spiritual health. I had heeded the call, examined my story, and found the meanings that had been made up by an upset 10-year old. I transformed my life and habits completely in all 5 of these areas (mind, emotions, body, spirit, and story). I discovered and applied for myself the Freedom Framework—the very same method for finding and fixing the root sources of *dis-ease* that I am presenting to you in this book.

No One-Size-Fits-All Cure for Anything

We are not "standardized" people and therefore there can never be standardized interventions for what we want to think of as standard problems. There is no such thing. This is the lie of "evidence-based medicine." Our scientific research is done on random samplings of small groups of the population and then we attempt to extrapolate data that we can apply to everyone. That is why the list of side effects for every medication ever invented is so long. We react to our food, medications, sleep, exercise, thoughts, experiences, climate, age, and toxins very differently. There is no diet that is going to solve autoimmunity for every person. Everything must be individualized to fit you as the unique person you are.

Health *and* disease are both byproducts of your genetics plus your physical, mental, and emotional digestive health. Vitality is a result of your exposure to toxins of all kinds, and your ability to detoxify or rid yourself of the toxins you have been exposed to. It is a result of your ability to assimilate the nutrients from your food, thoughts, and emotions and to eliminate what you do not need. This process leads to vitality, or what I think of as life force. Ayurveda calls this ojas. I call it "O Juice."

The remainder of this book will give you the knowledge to help you personalize your own food plan and lifestyle choices to enhance your ojas, so you can live to your potential with all of the energy and life force you need.

In my first book, *Solving the Autoimmune Puzzle,* I provided you with a set of instructions for how to put your puzzle together, so you don't have to wander around desperately trying to find answers to why you are still trapped by your weight, your hormones, autoimmune disease, your lack of energy and vitality, low libido, mood swings, digestive issues, heart problems, blood sugar imbalances, thyroid disorders, infertility, menstrual problems, and any other pain you are experiencing. In this book, I am providing you with a set of templates, master recipes you can use to learn how to feed yourself so that you are nourished and can fulfill your life purpose.

Autoimmunity takes many shapes; hence, there are many kinds of puzzles. Let's begin with the big picture on the front of the box before we dump all the puzzle pieces out on the table.

CHAPTER TWO

A Body at War with Itself Can Never Win

"It is easier to change a man's religion than to change his diet."

—Margaret Mead

What is Autoimmunity?

The word "autoimmune" means that your immune system has begun to attack you. Autoimmunity means your immune system has lost the ability to differentiate between you and the foreign invaders it is designed to protect you from, such as bacteria, fungi, parasites, and viruses. An autoimmune disease develops when your immune system, which defends your body against disease, decides your healthy cells are foreign. As your hypervigilant immune system attacks healthy cells and body tissue, you can end up with damaged organs and body systems and ultimately cancer, even death.

The American Autoimmune Related Disease Association (AARDA) reports there are 50 million Americans who have one or more autoimmune diseases, and that number is rising. Autoimmune illnesses are the second most common cause of chronic illness in the United States. Researchers have identified over 145 different autoimmune diseases and that number is also rising. I am not alone in considering this one of the most alarming health crises of our time.

Autoimmune diseases will often fluctuate Uncle SAM model focuses on relieving symptoms by using toxic prescription drugs and over-the-counter medications. The commonly used immunosuppressant treatments and non-steroidal anti-inflammatory drugs (NSAIDs) used as pain relievers lead to devastating long-term side effects while making the pharmaceutical industry hundreds of millions, if not billions, of dollars a year.

Because many autoimmune diseases have similar symptoms, people can go for years undiagnosed. In the current Uncle SAM model of matching drugs to symptoms, vague and often overlapping symptoms have made diagnosis difficult and medical delivery of care convoluted in the extreme. When you develop one autoimmune disease, you are 75% likely to develop another, and another. Why? Because we are not addressing the root causes of autoimmunity. We are chasing symptoms, and people are getting sicker and sicker and dying because of a healthcare paradigm that is not working.

A Disease by Any Other Name Is Still a Disease

More and more diseases are being classified as autoimmune as our understanding of the immune system and its interplay with genetics broadens. Often my patients will come to my office with the misinformed idea that their autoimmune disease originates in the body tissue the immune system is attacking. For example, rheumatoid arthritis originates in the joints, or Hashimoto's thyroiditis originates in the thyroid. This view is incorrect, and we will get into more detail on this in Chapter Three when we explore how to heal leaky gut.

Autoimmune disease is a disease of an immune system that has become hypervigilant. Because 70% of the immune system is contained in the gut, having a healthy digestive system is essential when we want to reverse inflammation and autoimmunity.

Will the Archer Please Put Down the Bow and Arrows?

The symptoms of autoimmune disease are as varied as the target organs the immune system may attack. However, remember that autoimmunity is a result of several root causes that have usually been out of balance for a long time before diagnosis. This is another one of the pearls of ancient wisdom Ayurvedic medicine provides. We will explore Ayurveda more in Chapter Five. Long before full-blown disease, there are usually warning signs of worsening imbalance. One of the most common signs your body gives you that something is wrong is fatigue.

We, as women don't usually tolerate fatigue, and our "no-pain-no-gain" work ethos can drive us to reach for a caffeinated beverage, pill, or a sugar-packed food source rather than have our forward motion impeded. We tell ourselves we have to bring home the bacon, fry it up in a pan, and look hot at the same time. This need to look like Wonder Woman is destroying the male/female balance on the planet and is literally killing each of us as we develop autoimmunity and cancer in numbers never before known in our history.

In the Uncle SAM model, autoimmune diseases are classified and treated according to the target organ or tissue being attacked. Picture an archer with a quiver of arrows on her back and a bow in her hand. She is looking at a target in the distance with an arrow strung and bow pulled back, and she's ready to release it. As it zings through the air, we doctors are standing by the target trying to move it around.

That makes no sense and doesn't work. If we successfully move the target and the arrow misses, the archer will just release another arrow towards a different target. Instead, we need to gently tap the archer on the shoulder and ask him to put his bow and quiver of arrows down. We need to teach him a more peaceful way. We can instruct him to shoot only when there is true and present danger. You'll see how to do this when we examine the Freedom Framework later in this chapter.

The Return of the Archer

Even after you have taught the archer (your immune system) to become a more peaceful warrior, she will take up arms once again if she is signaled to do so repeatedly. She will once again become reactive and hypervigilant in search of danger if she is signaled by the mind that you are in danger. What is the alarm that will set her off once again? You and your response to stress.

When you believe yourself to be overwhelmed with the stress of your life, your mind will active the neurotransmitter chemicals of the brain to alert your body to go into fight or flight. When you think you are a zebra being chased by a lion and are in fear of being eaten, you won't be able to digest your food, thoughts, or emotions properly. When you're reacting from the fight-or-flight stress response system, you have activated your reptilian brain, which is unable to forgive, have fun, be friendly, have faith, flourish, or engage in functional relationships with other human beings.

The whole point of this cookbook is to help you find and fix the root causes that are blocking your flow towards nourishing food that will help you flourish as the person you are meant to be.

Stress Can Also Be Medicine

We often hear that stress is bad for you. You might have heard that stress is the cause of all illness. This is not true. It's your *perception* of your stress—your belief that the stress level you have is not manageable—that activates the fight-or-flight response system. You actually need stress in your life. You need just *enough* stress to keep you challenged and motivated. It is when you *perceive* your challenges are overwhelming, too overwhelming to handle, that your immune system is activated and you create what I call the autoimmune mindset.

When you have activated your stress response system, your hormones relay the messages from the brain to the adrenal glands. The adrenal glands sit on top of your kidneys. The adrenal glands will then release a stress hormone called cortisol.

Cortisol is a hormone. Almost every cell contains receptors for cortisol, so cortisol

will behave according to the cell it's acting upon. When cortisol is balanced, it will help control blood-sugar levels, fluid balance, help you wake up in the morning, reduce inflammation, help with memory, and aid in fertility and blood pressure regulation. Cortisol, like stress, is not bad.

Too much cortisol, though, can be damaging. When you are chronically releasing cortisol because you are chronically overwhelmed and chronically sending danger messages through your relay system, you will start seeing tissue and organ breakdown in your body, as well as weight gain and a decrease in your libido. This is one of the root causes of leaky gut (which we will look at in Chapter Three). Cortisol breaks down the protective lining of your intestinal wall. Prolonged cortisol release can interfere with sleep or cause you to wake up fatigued in the morning even if you did get 8 hours of sleep. It can cause weight gain in the belly area, even when you are exercising and eating well. It affects your immune system, contributes to joint pain and inflammation, tanks your libido level, and can cause anxiety and depression, all of which are common symptoms in autoimmune disease. This is a primary cause of hormone imbalance in both men and women.

The Stress Response and How it Impacts Your Hormones

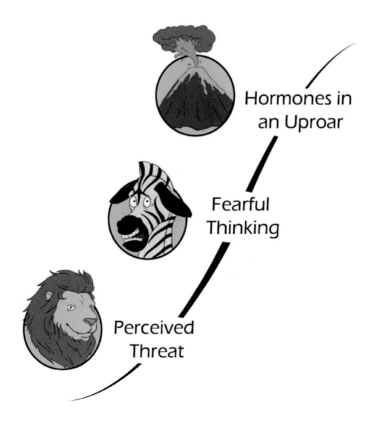

Hormones in an Uproar

Fearful Thinking

Perceived Threat

The Rest-and-Digest System

You are wired to go into the fight-or-flight response system when there is danger or when you perceive danger, just as a zebra does when being chased by a lion. This allows you to respond instantly to a clear threat to your survival. Your body is then meant to go back into balance after you have gotten to safety, just like the zebra's does. When you are out of danger, you can then activate your rest-and-digest system, which is necessary for proper digestion and assimilation of nutrients, fertility and reproduction, a healthy body mass index and weight, and the complete excretion of toxins from your mind and body. Unfortunately, in our fast-paced, productivity-oriented culture, we are not getting enough time to *rest-and-digest* or *feed-and-breed* because we are hanging out in *fight-or-flight* so much of the time. I cannot count how many of my patients break down and cry or get outright angry with me when I suggest self-care activities designed to tone their *rest-and-digest* system.

Important note: If you feel like crying or biting my head off when I tell you it's important for you to prepare healthy foods to eat, you have adrenal fatigue.

Here's what I know is true. If you feel stressed about scheduling some time every single day to feed yourself nourishing foods, then you have an autoimmune mindset and are either on your way to autoimmune disease or you already have one—or more. But that doesn't mean the die is cast. As I experienced, and as many of my patients have experienced, this process of heading towards autoimmune disease is reversible. Let's take a brief look at how.

The Freedom Framework

You are your own unique puzzle. You have your own unique blend of genetics, toxic exposure, past experiences, current stress, dietary choices, and digestive health. The Freedom Framework empowers you to investigate any health issue you have at the root cause level and bring your vitality onto a whole new trajectory.

When you see a puzzle you want to put together, the first thing you do is dump all of the pieces out on the table. You then start turning them over, looking for the corner and edge pieces. The four corner pieces of any chronic inflammatory puzzle are:

1) Genetics

2) Leaky gut

3) Toxins

4) Past stress and adverse childhood experiences

In my earlier book, *Solving the Autoimmune Puzzle*, I introduced the Freedom Framework.* I teach this framework to my integrative medicine health coach students at the Academy for Integrative Medicine. It is the framework I use for exploring and solving your unique health puzzle.

---

*Here I'm going to give you just a brief overview of the Freedom Framework. If you want to take a deeper dive into it, please see my previous book, *Solving the Autoimmune Puzzle: The Woman's Guide to Reclaiming Emotional Freedom and Vibrant Health.*

I've boiled the process of the Freedom Framework down to the following sets of four:

- The Four Pillars or Frame of Your Autoimmune Puzzle

- The Four Corner Pieces of Your Autoimmune Puzzle

- The Four Rs of Healing in the Center of Your Autoimmune Puzzle

The Four Pillars of the Freedom Framework

The four pillars of the Freedom Framework can be applied to any chronic illness, any inflammatory process, any autoimmune disease. The four pillars are:

1) un-Cover root cause(s) in the body, mind, heart, spirit, and in your story.

2) Confront the data collected through laboratory testing and the feedback from your body such as your bowel movements, weight, energy level, sleep quality, libido level.

3) Connect your beliefs, behaviors, and dietary choices with the data you just confronted.

4) Create the life you want to be living with full intention.

Figure 1: The Freedom Framework with the four pillars or frame and the 4 corner pieces of the autoimmune puzzle

The BIG Pieces of the Puzzle

There are four corner pieces to the puzzle of autoimmune disease. These four corner pieces are scientifically validated common causes of autoimmune disease. These will be the anchor pieces to your puzzle. They are:

1) Your genetics

2) Environmental toxins

3) Leaky gut

4) Trauma

Past trauma and current-day stress affect your food choices. Those food choices impact the health of your digestive system and can cause leaky gut. Some of the environmental toxins, such as gut infections and viruses, can cause you to crave sugar and junk food. All of this will affect the expression of your genetics. So you see, food is a part of the whole puzzle.

Figure 2: The 4 corner pieces, or root causes, of autoimmune disease

The 4Rs of Healing

We live in an instant gratification society that likes to focus on quick fixes and magic pills. We are all incredibly busy with tight schedules. However, the magic pill theory simply doesn't work. Why do I say that? In spite of spending millions, or rather, billions, of dollars on healthcare, research, and drug development, the numbers of women (and men and children) being diagnosed with autoimmune diseases continues to escalate. There is no magic pill, no magic wand, and no magic diet. However, there are the "4 Rs" of gut healing, which are the centerpieces of your puzzle.

Functional medicine and the ancient science of Ayurvedic medicine both focus on getting to the root cause of illness. These 4Rs of gut healing will help you put your puzzle together and ultimately help you heal the root causes of your inflammation or autoimmunity. The 4Rs are:

1) **R**emove what is toxic or unhealthy.

2) **R**eplace what you removed with healthy alternatives.

3) **R**epair your relationship with food, self, others, life, and Spirit.

4) **R**ebalance your life to regain energy through self-care.

The Autoimmune Mindset

This book is not just about food. Ayurvedic medicine tells us that autoimmune disease is anger turned against oneself. Girls are often positively reinforced for being "good," "helpful," and "quiet." Women are considered aggressive, abrasive, and un-feminine when they express their feelings and speak their truth. If you have an autoimmune disease, you have a body attacking itself—no, killing itself. Women are diagnosed with 80% of the over 145 identified autoimmune diseases (that number is still growing). Several autoimmune diseases, including lupus, rheumatoid arthritis, Hashimoto's thyroiditis, myasthenia gravis, and multiple sclerosis, afflict women anywhere from two to 10 times more often than they do men.

Yes, our sex hormones, our x chromosomes, and a history of pregnancy all play a role in the development of autoimmune disease, but there are other important pieces to the autoimmune puzzle in women as well. One of those pieces is what I call the autoimmune mindset. The autoimmune mindset is formed in childhood and impacts your health in adulthood. It's the way you *digested* your early experiences, your thoughts, and your feelings. I want to help you improve your digestion on all levels, not just the physical. This cookbook will give you some recipes for improving your digestive fire in your mind and heart as well as in your body. When you are not digesting efficiently, your food is doing what we call putrefying. Yuck! That means rotting or decaying instead of absorbing, assimilating, and nourishing your cells.

Healing Your Emotional Wounds

How we learned to digest our childhood experiences, thoughts, and feelings largely determines how we subconsciously digest our present experiences, thoughts, and feelings. So yes, there are hundreds of toxins in addition to the environmental pollutants and toxicants you usually hear about. I am speaking of the thoughts and feelings that make you feel fearful, anxious, guilty, or ashamed. These too are toxins and mess with your immune system and hormone levels and impact your ability to digest the food you are learning to make from this cookbook.

Your thoughts and feelings are digested by your mind and heart much the same way food is digested by your digestive system. What you get from food is nourishment that gives you energy, vitality, and continued life as you create new cells from nutrients. What do you get from your thoughts and feelings? First you have a feeling, then a thought, and then you take action. So nourishing thoughts and feelings generate actions that allow you to live your life purpose. As food provides nourishment to create new cells, healthy thoughts and feelings generate actions that "create" your life.

Painful feelings and thoughts, on the other hand, are held in the body if they are not processed well. Early painful experiences can leave a "button" exposed for others to push later. If someone or something pushes that button, you will activate your stress response system. Unless you consciously change how you perceive and react to stress in your life, you will continue in the same pattern. It takes conscious awareness to change the patterns you have been repeating throughout your life, and often it takes very specialized trauma healing psychotherapy.

There are many thoughts, beliefs, and feelings that can create a hypervigilant immune system and play havoc with the hormones and immune function in your body. In fact, this is where we can be the least free—in our minds. On pages 69-72 I list 7 feelings that are present in people with an autoimmune mindset. I encourage you to spend some time thinking of others that might be keeping you stuck. These feelings and emotions and how well you digest them are as important as the food recipes I have provided later in this book.

CHAPTER THREE

Leaky Gut

What is leaky gut?

The term Leaky Gut Syndrome is also known as intestinal permeability syndrome. When your intestinal lining becomes porous, undigested food molecules, yeast, toxins, and other waste products that would not normally get through what is supposed to be a contained system, escape freely into your bloodstream.

Remember your intestinal lining is the first line of defense for your immune system. The exterior layers of intestinal cells, or epithelial cells, are linked by "tight junctions." The microvilli at the ends of these cells aid in the absorption of digested nutrients and then send them into the bloodstream. If these tight junctions loosen, the gut lining will become porous and allow molecules to flow directly into the bloodstream.

Once these molecules escape into the blood stream, your immune system mounts an attack. Your liver will try to screen out the "foreign invaders" that the damaged intestinal wall can no longer hold back. The waste, undigested food, and microbial toxins that enter the bloodstream when you have leaky gut wind up in the liver, whose job it is to detoxify and dump these poisons. Under ordinary circumstances, the liver is taxed just by processing the daily waste created by cell and organ activity. With leaky gut, there is a larger load and eventually the liver becomes saturated

and it will not be capable of this level of detoxification. As a result, toxins are returned to the blood stream. If this toxicity, or ama as Ayurveda calls it, settles into the cells, the inflammatory process can lead to genetic mutations and ultimately autoimmune disease and even cancer.

In such a situation, the immune system is on the attack and inflammation is the byproduct of this war you are waging with yourself. There is no winner when you are attacking you. Your body is fighting itself by fighting what you eat. Your joints might begin to hurt, your skin could develop a rash, you will likely feel fatigued and gain extra weight. If this process goes unchecked, you will begin to develop autoimmune disease as each layer of tissue, or what Ayurveda calls dhatus, becomes more and more inflamed. You will be more sensitive to chemicals, foods (even those you used to be able to eat or those thought of as healthy), the environment, and susceptible to infections such as the Epstein-Barr virus. You could develop sinus congestion, itchy ears, digestive issues, brain fog, and headaches.

If you take a look at figures 3 and 4 you will see this process illustrated.

What Causes Leaky Gut?

Your gut wall houses 70 percent of the cells that make up your immune system. This is why it was written in Ayurvedic texts that

From Leaky Gut to Dis-ease

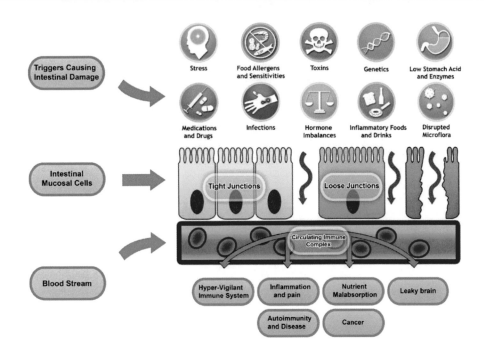

Figure 3: Progression from leaky gut to disease

the root of all disease (and wellness) starts in the digestive system. These early healers knew that digestive problems are linked to autoimmunity, allergies, fatigue, weight problems, mood disorders like depression and anxiety, sleep difficulties, dementia, and cancer. The gastrointestinal system affects the entire body and is now called our second genome. Yes, it even impacts how we express our genetics.

You have over 100 trillion microscopic organisms living in your gut; these can be organized into 500 different species. These little critters account for 3-5 pounds of your body weight and help you break down your food and keep your gut wall healthy. Even in a perfect world, your gut has a hard time keeping you balanced and your digestion running smoothly. In the frenetic world we live in today, filled with fast food, eating on the run, and over-booked schedules, there are several factors that contribute to leaky gut.

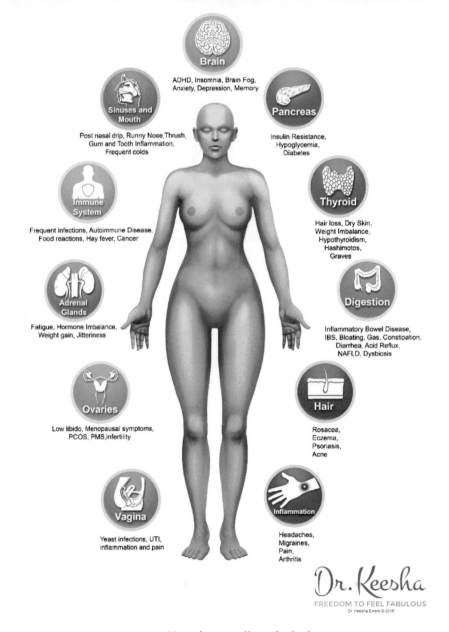

Figure 4: How the gut affects the body

Here are some of the most common causes of leaky gut.

- **Medications**: Acid-blocking drugs, chemotherapy, steroids, anti-inflammatories, antibiotics, and the oral birth control pill can damage the gut wall and inhibit healthy digestion.

- **The Standard American (SAD) diet**: Our calorie-rich, nutrient-poor diet of processed foods causes the wrong bacteria and yeast to grow in the gut, leading to an unhealthy gut ecosystem.

- **Toxins**: Mercury fillings; chemicals in the environment, home, personal hygiene products, and your mattress; and mold toxins can create a toxic overload that can damage the gut lining.

- **Low Stomach Acid and Digestive Enzymes**: Stress, the removal of your gall bladder, a deficiency in zinc and other minerals, and acid-blocking medications can all impair proper enzyme and stomach acid production.

- **Gut Infections**: Yeast, small intestinal bacteria overgrowth (SIBO), parasites, and a bacteria called heliobacter pylori can all impact your digestive function, and consequently your immune function.

- **Stress**: The stress hormone cortisol that is released by the adrenal glands when you are under chronic stress will alter your gut nervous system and break down your gut lining. This is a primary cause of leaky gut and an unhealthy ecosystem of gut microbes.

- **Food Sensitivities and Inflammatory Foods**: With leaky gut, nutrients will be absorbed before they are fully digested. The body's immune system will tag some of these foods as foreign invaders. The body will see the inflammatory reaction your immune system has to these foods as yet another stressful event, causing more gut-wall-destroying cortisol to be released from your adrenal glands. And so the cycle continues.

- **Infections**: When the gut lining is damaged, the body is more vulnerable to bacterial, fungal, parasitic, and viral infections, which become resistant to treatment. These resistant microbes cause doctors to prescribe more and more antibiotics, which causes candida (yeast) overgrowth. Candida causes more gut-wall inflammation, and so again the vicious cycle continues. With the gut wall now more and more permeable, or leaky, the yeast and bacteria can escape into the bloodstream and settle into any area of the body, including the brain, sinuses, bladder, vaginal wall, and skin.

- **Hormonal imbalances**: Leaky gut can cause a problem with blood-sugar regulation, which can cause a decrease in testosterone and an increase in estrogen in men, putting them at risk for muscle wasting, weight gain, and prostate cancer. The same issue can cause an increase in testosterone and an increase in the wrong kind of estrogen in women. This increase in testosterone in women can lead to hair loss from the head, extra hair on the face, weight issues, and infertility. The increase in estrogen can put women at risk for estrogen-related cancers.

Yes, most of us are subject to one or more of these factors, which is why leaky gut is so common. In fact, every one of my clients has leaky gut to some extent. This means undigested food molecules escape into the blood stream and activate the immune system, which is wired to attack anything it senses that is "not you." This attack leads to inflammation, which can show up in a host of ways, eventually developing into any number of diseases. Remember, a hypervigilant immune system creates "auto-immunity" or "you attacking you." You are indeed what you eat, and if your immune system is not friends with what you eat, it turns on you.

How to Fix Leaky Gut

The most common symptom I see in my patients with autoimmune disease, and therefore leaky gut, is multiple food sensitivities. When partially digested food proteins work their way through your gut wall and into your bloodstream, your immune system will rightly take offense. Your immune system is wired to attack anything that is "not you." This offensive reaction will mean you develop food sensitivities that will multiply in number and severity the longer you do not treat your leaky gut. Sticking your head in the sand and ignoring the feedback your body is giving you will only cause it to turn up the volume.

Food Allergies vs. Food Sensitivities

Food sensitivities are not necessarily food allergies. When your lips go numb or you break out in hives anywhere from 20 minutes to two hours after eating a food, this is known as an IgE food allergy. This can be picked up when you go to see your allergist, who will run a radioallergosorbent blood test (RAST) and/or a skin allergy test. These tests do not detect IgG reactions from your immune system.

A food sensitivity is a non-IgE reaction, which is characterized by the measurement of IgG antibodies to food proteins not being tolerated in a person's body. An IgG food sensitivity is a delayed hypersensitivity reaction. It can take four hours to four days for symptoms, silent or overt, to appear after eating the offending food. This distinction is often lost on the Uncle SAM model of healthcare. IgG food sensitivity testing is often dismissed as invalid because, like IgE testing, it too is limited.

Like IgE testing, IgG testing only measures one mechanism of the immune response. There are often several non-immune responses, such as a histamine intolerance and gut-wall damage from lectins, in people with autoimmune disease. I use Mediator Release Testing (MRT) to make sure as many factors are tested for that could be creating critical mass for the body. The release of mediators like histamines, cytokines, or prostaglandins from the white blood cells are usually triggered by the activation of the immune system, whether it's IgG, IgE, IgA, IgM or a complement reaction. The complexity of the immune system is what makes food sensitivity testing controversial. The MRT methodology is the one I have found that simplifies the leaky gut healing process and covers the most bases.

As listed above, there are many causes for leaky gut, but they can be distilled down to four main categories: 1) food, 2) stress, 3) toxins, and 4) bacterial imbalances/infections. In this book we are focusing on food.

The SAD Food Program

Sugar, GMO's, pasteurized dairy, gluten, and the phytates and lectins found in grains and soy are the most common foods that cause inflammation and damage your intestinal lining. Sprouting and fermenting grains reduces phytates and lectins, which can make some of these grains more digestible. However, when you are embarking on a program to heal leaky gut, it's best to just stay away from these foods. Unfortunately, many households have gotten used to the standard American diet (SAD) that includes eating from cans, packages, boxes, and fast-food restaurants, which pack their products with leaky-gut causing ingredients.

You are going to want to go from SAD to GLAD (**G**luten-free, **L**ectin-free, **A**ll-natural **D**iet). There are several versions of GLAD programs that are popular right now. Some are vegan or vegetarian. Others are paleo, autoimmune paleo, ketogenic, or more specific, such as the Specific Carbohydrate Diet and the GAPs diet. Others use a dosha-specific Ayurvedic plan. (See Chapter Five.) I have found that, like everything else in life, there is no one size that fits everyone.

Choosing the Right Food Plan for You

No matter where you are on the autoimmune spectrum, there are certain foods in the SAD that are not good for anyone and I recommend you eliminate them completely. If you choose to indulge very occasionally in a favorite item on this list, please do it slowly and mindfully with love and joy and avoid consuming it fearfully or with shame or guilt.

One of the most damaging eating disorders functional medicine has unwittingly propagated is called orthorexia. Orthorexia is anxious and obsessive behavior in pursuit of a healthy diet. This eating disorder creates so much fear that people who suffer with it begin to think of food as an enemy. Specific foods are classified as good or bad. What orthorexics don't realize is that, like anorexia or bulimia, this obsessive and adversarial relationship with food causes the fight-or-flight nervous system to engage (which shuts down your digestive system) right at meal time. Meal time is when you want your digestive system functional so you can digest and absorb and eliminate properly.

The items I am going to recommend you eliminate from your diet are not to be classified as "bad"; rather, just think of them as non-foods. When I talk about whole foods, nourishing foods, disease-reversing foods, I am talking about the food your great grandparents likely ate if they had a garden and lived close to the land. Much of what we call food today is not even food. The definition of food is, *any nutritious substance that people eat or drink in order to maintain life and growth.* The substances

I am asking you to remove from your diet are not food, and therefore are not contributing to life or growth for you but rather to disease and deterioration.

Basic non-food substances to eliminate from your diet if you want to flourish and thrive

- Gluten
- Processed, packaged, boxed, canned items
- Pasteurized non-organic dairy products
- Sugar, high fructose corn syrup, and other artificial sweeteners
- Chemicals such as added flavoring, artificial coloring, preservatives
- Toxins from contaminated farmed animals and fish
- Substances that come from animals who have been treated with cruelty
- Hydrogenated and trans fats
- Alcohol
- GMOs and non-organic foods
- Stimulants such as caffeine
- Depressants such as marijuana

More advanced list of foods to remove when you have leaky gut

- Grains (you can add sprouted versions of non-gluten containing grains later in the healing process and see if you tolerate them)
- Legumes (you can add sprouted versions in later in the healing process and see if you tolerate them)
- Natural sweeteners from coconut, maple, rice, dates, agave, stevia, and xylitol (in the beginning of your healing)
- Soy
- High glycemic index fruit (see chart)
- Vegetables high in starch (see chart)
- Meats that have been treated with antibiotics and chemicals and raised inhumanely
- Eggs
- Tomatoes, white potatoes, and eggplants
- Peppers including bell peppers and hot peppers
- Spices such as curries, paprika, and chili powder
- Nuts and seeds
- Fried or fast food
- Chocolate
- Dried fruit

FRUITS

Food	GI Value
Cherries	22
Grapefruit	25
Prunes	29
Apricots, dried	30
Apple	38
Peach, canned in juice	38
Pear, fresh	38
Plum	39
Strawberries	40
Orange, Navel	42
Peach, fresh	42
Pear, canned	43
Grapes	46
Mango	51
Banana	52
Fruit Cocktail	55
Papaya	56
Raisins	56
Apricots, fresh	57
Kiwi	58
Figs, dried	61
Apricots, canned	64
Cantaloupe	65
Pineapple, fresh	66
Watermelon	72
Dates	103

VEGETABLES

Food	GI Value
Broccoli	10
Cabbage	10
Lettuce	10
Mushrooms	10
Onions	10
Red Peppers	10
Carrots	49
Green peas	48
Corn, fresh	60
Beets	64
Pumpkin	75
Parsnips	97

BEANS

Food	GI Value
Chana Dal	8
Chickpeas, dried	28
Kidney Beans, dried	28
Lentils	29
Lima Beans (frozen)	32
Yellow Split Peas	32
Chickpeas, canned	42
Blackeyed Peas, canned	42
Baked Beans	48
Kidney Beans, canned	52

SWEETENERS

Food	GI Value
Stevia	0
Yacon syrup	1
xylitol	12
Fructose	19
Coconut palm sugar	35
Brown rice syrup	45
Marmalade	48
Honey	55
Evaporated cane juice	55
Molasses	55
Sorghum syrup	55
High fructose corn syrup	58
Jam	65
Brown sugar	65
Sucrose (white sugar)	68
Maple Syrup	76

SNACKS

Food	GI Value
Hummus	6
Peanuts	15
Walnuts	15
Cashews	22
M & M Peanut Candies	33
Milk Chocolate	43
Potato Chips	57
Kudos Bar	62
Corn Chips	63
Popcorn	72
Jelly Beans	78
Pretzels	83

POTATOES

Food	GI Value
Yam	37
Sweet	44
New	57
Canned	65
White skinned mashed	70
French Fries	75
Baked	85
Instant Mashed	86
Red Skinned, boiled	88

CRACKERS

Food	GI Value
Stoned Wheat Thins	67
Ryvita Crispbread	69
Melba Toast	70
Kavli Crispbread	71
Soda Crackers	74
Graham Crackers	74
Water crackers	78
Rice Cakes	82
Rice Crackers	91

CEREALS

Food	GI Value
Muesli	43
Bran Buds	47
Oat Bran	55
Bran Chex	58
Raisin Bran	61
Cream of Wheat	66
Quick (One Minute) Oats	66
Pancakes	67
Puffed Wheat	67
Special K	69
Grapenuts	71
Bran Flakes	74
Cheerios	74
Cream of Wheat Instant	74
Shredded Wheat	75
Waffles	76
Rice Krispies	82
Corn Chex	83
Corn Flakes	92

GRAINS

Food	GI Value
Barley, pearled	25
Converted, White	38
Long grain, White	44
Buckwheat	54
Brown	55
Basmati	58
Couscous	65
Cornmeal	68
Aborio	69
Short grain, White	72
Instant, White	87
Wild rice	87
Glutinous (Sticky)	98

BREADS

Food	GI Value
Pumpernickel	41
Sourdough	53
Stone Ground whole wheat	53
Pita, whole wheat	57
Whole Meal Rye	58
Hamburger bun	61
Croissant	67
Taco Shell	68
White	70
Bagel	72
Kaiser roll	73
Bread stuffing	74
Whole wheat (100%)	77
French Baguette	95

PASTA

Food	GI Value
Fettuccini (egg)	32
Spaghetti, whole wheat	37
Spaghetti, white	38
Star Pastina	38
Spiral Pasta	43
Capellini	45
Linguine	46
Macaroni	47
Rice vermicelli	58

What to eat:

- 10-12 cups of a vegetables that encompass the whole rainbow of color

- Bone broth

- Clean protein with every meal

- One serving of low glycemic fruit per day (or none if you are trying to lose weight)

- Organic herbal tea and infusions

- Healthy fats such as ghee, coconut oil, and avocados

- Plenty of herb-infused or fruit-infused water, or plain water

- Fresh herbs and spices other than the ones I listed above

The lists I just gave you are by no means exhaustive. When you have followed this plan for 3 months, check in with your body. If your inflammation is not gone, you need to do some more in-depth functional medicine testing like I do in my practice. I don't talk about curing your autoimmunity, but rather reversing it. Why? Because if you follow the program I am laying out here and you begin to feel better, and then revert to your old ways of emotional reactivity, self-limiting beliefs and behaviors, and non-nourishing dietary choices, you will find yourself living with fatigue, weight problems, mood issues, inflammatory symptoms, and autoimmune disease again. I am sure I could re-instigate my rheumatoid arthritis if I started back on gluten, sugar, soy, grains, dairy, and

stuffing my feelings and ruminating on my past hurts and resentments again. My genetics are programmed for RA. It would be fairly easy to flip the autoimmune switch back on. I like living with full vitality, so I don't revert to my old ways. It's that simple.

The Misery-to-Motivation Ratio
People are willing to change their self-sabotaging behaviors to the degree that those behaviors are making them miserable. I have found this to be consistently true of human nature. I began noticing that my patients who were only mildly miserable were only willing to make a mild effort to reverse their autoimmunity. For example, if your fingers or toes feel cold or numb and turn white or blue in response to cold temperatures or stress you might have Raynaud's disease. It's easier to put some gloves on than it is to change your diet if your fingers are cold—unless you make the connection between your cold fingers and your gut and genetics. If you know those cold fingers are a harbinger of future disease, it can be more motivating.

My patients who come in whose sleep is tortured because of itching skin, anxiety, or heart palpitations are desperate to do whatever it takes to sleep again. Those who cannot stand to even feel the fabric of their clothing against their skin because of hives are willing and ready to do whatever it takes to feel "normal" once again. Those who are in constant pain and can no longer engage in the activities they once enjoyed with the people they love are motivated to do whatever they need to feel alive again. Some are motivated by the desire to play with grandchildren. Others want to go back to work, to hike again, to dance again, even to walk again. When I was diagnosed with RA, my motivator was not only my own lack of energy and joint pain; I also wanted my children to be raised by a fully present and vibrant mother.

Find Your Why

My why has evolved over the last 25 years. It's what keeps me from reverting back to old self-sabotaging destructive habits. I want to make sure that as I leave this life, I am not visited by the version of myself that I could have been and find that I have not met my potential. For me, not reaching my potential means I have wasted this lifetime. If I am not utterly grateful and appreciative for the life I have been granted, willing to take care of this amazing gift that is my body, and constantly challenging myself to utilize the gifts God has sent me here to share with my fellow beings, then I have not lived my purpose and that is my personal definition of hell.

That is my why for continuing to reframe and refine my beliefs, behaviors, and habits. It's to make sure I can shine a light for others who are floundering in the darkness of autoimmunity where I once was. This has taken me from being in an autoimmune mindset to being in a vitality mindset. I am no longer resistant to doing whatever it takes for me to expand and evolve and to help others do the same. This makes it much easier to make healthy choices to nourish my body, mind, heart, and spirit.

I encourage you to find your why. It's what will motivate you to make the life changes you are being challenged to make. It's so much easier to reach for a package

of chocolate chip cookies than to develop self-awareness when you are overwhelmed. Believe me, I know. I am hoping that you will not have to get to rock bottom misery before you are motivated to make the changes you need to be the most brilliant and vital version of yourself.

Test Don't Guess

The misery-to-motivation ratio is never so apparent as when we start talking about diet. I always test for food sensitivities in my patients with autoimmunity, and I repeat the test every 9-12 months while we are actively healing their leaky gut with supplements, personalized food programs, emotional healing, and mental reframing. I will often hear my new patients tell me they have already tried getting rid of gluten and it "didn't work." You have to have realistic expectations when you are healing a problem that has been in place for perhaps decades. If you have eliminated gluten for 2 weeks in the past and didn't feel better, it's because 2 weeks wasn't long enough and gluten wasn't the only thing you needed to eliminate. I start with the lists I gave you earlier and then begin to fine tune and personalize the program to each individual. I use genetic and organic acids testing to see if my patient needs to follow a vegetarian diet, a microbiome balancing protocol, reduce oxalates, watch tyramine or histamine, or follow a Mediterranean or paleo style plan.

If you are miserable with severe digestive symptoms and cannot tolerate many foods already, then start on a specific carbohydrate diet (SCD) plan. If your misery level is mild, start with a paleo diet, utilizing the food list I provided. If your genetics indicate meat puts you at a higher risk for heart disease and Alzheimer's disease, then modify both the SCD and the paleo diet to include wild fish, collagen, and egg white protein as sources of meat protein. Yes, collagen and egg whites come from animals. Collagen is also processed. However, neither contain the animal fats that a person with an APOe 4/4 gene cannot metabolize well. In the next section, we'll go into much more detail on specific dietary considerations.

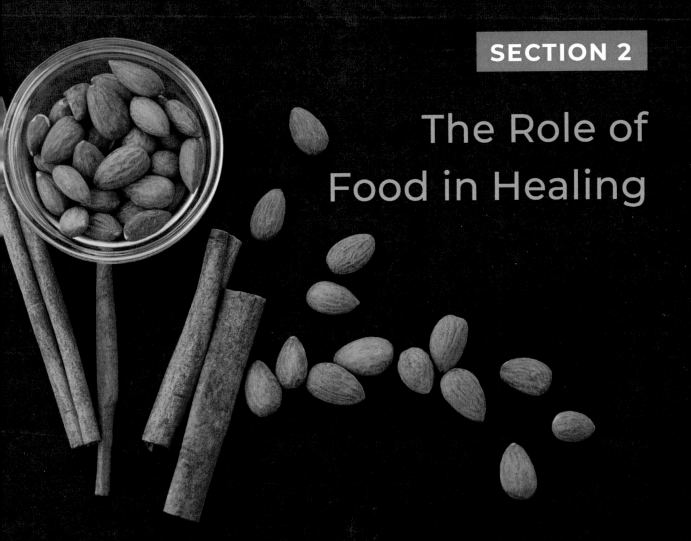

The Role of Food in Healing

CHAPTER FOUR

Some Specific Dietary Considerations

The Specific Carbohydrate Diet

The Specific Carbohydrate Diet (SCD) was developed in the 1950s by Dr. Sidney Haas. Yes, as far back as the 1950s, people were struggling with celiac and other autoimmune diseases. Dr. Haas treated the young daughter of Elaine Gottschall, who then went on to write the book that helped me reverse the worst of my oldest son's Asperger's Syndrome 45 years later. The name of the book is *Breaking the Vicious Cycle.*

The SCD is a program that removes processed, GMO, sugary, and starchy products from your diet. It has been used by thousands of people over the last 70+ years to heal digestive, immune, and mental imbalances. Like Ayurvedic medicine, the SCD principles recognize we are not all the same. Not every digestive tract can digest man-made chemicals and highly processed carbohydrates and sugars. Any improperly digested carbohydrate can be used as food for unwelcome gut microbes, such as yeast, bacteria, or parasites. When an overgrowth of any of these organisms occurs, they reproduce using the sugars you are feeding them. Then they release toxins and acids into your digestive system, which can cause damage and inhibit nutrient absorption and the proper elimination of waste. The build-up of these acids and toxins creates the vicious cycle that worsens leaky gut.

The SCD eliminates these sugars, thus cutting the organisms off from their food supply, and then begins to restore gut flora so the intestinal wall can heal as inflammation is reduced.

The SCD is introduced using easy-to-digest foods and is then advanced with more complex foods as the gut heals. It can be individualized to fit your specific digestive state of injury or health. The idea is that as your inflammation reduces, gut wall repairs, healthy flora balance is restored, and disease is reversed, your food options will expand as your tolerance expands.

FODMAPS and Your Diet

FODMAP is an acronym that refers to specific carbohydrates that can be difficult for some people to digest under certain circumstances. FODMAP stands for Fermentable Oligo-Di-Monosaccharides and Polyols. If you find that foods containing FODMAPs cause gas, bloating, upper epi-gastric pain, diarrhea, and/or constipation, you might be someone who is not tolerating FODMAPs for any of the following reasons:

- Small intestinal bacterial overgrowth (SIBO)
- Overgrowth of harmful microbes (dysbiosis)

- Low stomach-acid levels
  (Hypochlorhydria)

- Gut pathogens from other regions of
  the world

Foods high in FODMAPs are as follows:

Vegetables and Legumes
Garlic
Onions
Artichoke
Asparagus
Baked beans
Bananas, ripe
Beetroot, fresh
Black beans
Black eyed peas
Broad beans
Butter beans
Cassava
Cauliflower
Celery
Falafel
Fermented cabbage e.g. sauerkraut
Haricot beans
Kidney beans
Lima beans
Leek bulb
Mange Tout
Mixed vegetables
Mung beans
Mushrooms
Peas, sugar snap
Pickled vegetables
Red kidney beans
Savoy Cabbage
Soy beans
Split peas
Scallions
Shallots
Taro

Fruit
Apples
Apricots
Avocado
Blackberries
Blackcurrants
Boysenberry
Cherries
Currants
Dates
Figs
Goji berries
Grapefruit
Guava, unripe
Lychee
Mango
Nectarines
Paw paw, dried
Peaches
Pears
Persimmon
Pineapple, dried
Plums
Pomegranate
Prunes
Raisins
Sea buckthorns
Sultanas
Tamarillo

Tinned fruit in apple / pear juice
Watermelon

Meat
Chorizo
Sausages

Wheat-containing products
Biscuits
Bread
Breadcrumbs
Cakes
Croissants
Muffins
Pastries
Pasta
Udon noodles
Wheatgerm
Almond meal
Amaranth flour
Barley
Bran cereals

Bread
Granary bread
Multigrain bread
Naan
Oatmeal bread
Pumpernickel bread
Roti
Sourdough with kamut

Nuts and miscellaneous grains
Cashews
Cous cous
Einkorn flour
Freekeh
Gnocchi
Granola bars
Muesli cereal
Muesli bar

Pistachios
Rye
Rye crispbread
Semolina
Spelt flour

Condiments, Dips, Sweets, Sweeteners and Spreads
Agave
Caviar dip
Fructose
Fruit bar
Gravy, if it contains onion
High fructose corn syrup (HFCS)
Hummus
Honey
Jam
Jam, strawberry, containing HFCS
Molasses
Pesto sauce
Quince paste
Relish
Fermented vegetables
Sugar free sweets containing polyols – usually ending in -ol or isomalt

Sweeteners
Inulin
Isomalt
Maltitol
Mannitol
Sorbitol
Xylitol
Tahini paste
Tzatziki dip

Prebiotic Foods
Watch labels for the following:
FOS – fructooligosaccharides
Inulin
Oligofructose

Drinks and Protein Powders
Beer
Coconut water
Fruit and herbal teas with apple added
Fruit juices in large quantities
Fruit juices made of apple, pear, mango
Kombucha
Malted chocolate flavored drink
Orange juice in quantities over 100 ml
Rum
Sodas containing high fructose corn syrup (HFCS)
Soy milk
Sports drinks
Whey protein powder

Tea
Chai tea
Herbal teas
Oolong tea
Wine

Dairy
Buttermilk
Cream cheese
Ricotta cheese
Cream
Custard
Gelato
Ice cream
Kefir
Cow milk
Goat milk
Evaporated milk
Sheep's milk
Sour cream
Yogurt
Whey

Flavor Enhancers
Carob powder

If any of these foods cause any of the symptoms I listed above, it's a good idea to get functional medicine testing done. You never want to have to avoid such a long list of foods for the rest of your life. It's good to just do the testing, follow the treatment protocol, and make sure you re-test to confirm that the issue is fixed. I have patients who have chased issues for years without success, either because they didn't follow their treatment protocol well, or they never returned to get re-tested. Always test rather than guess. Your body has a way of letting you know when something is wrong and it's not always pleasant if you ignore it for too long.

Oxalates and Inflammation

Oxalates (or oxalic acid) are a naturally occurring compound in some foods and are also produced in small amounts by the liver.

Oxalates help protect plants from their predators by their bitter taste. They can also prevent proper digestion in humans of foods that contain them. If you eat a lot of foods high in oxalates, they can make it impossible for your body to absorb nutrients, such as calcium. This is why people who get frequent kidney stones need to eat a diet low in oxalates. They likely have a genetic issue that makes the effects of oxalates worse.

When a patient comes to me with a painful inflammatory joint or skin issue, who does not respond fully to the dietary regimen laid out in the recipes of this book, I will do a functional medicine test to see if they are having trouble with oxalates. People who often respond well to a reduction of oxalates are those with autoimmune diseases and those who are following a restrictive diet. Some of the frequently eaten foods in dietary protocols like SCD, Paleo, or vegan are high in oxalates.

Some of the highest oxalate foods:

Dark chocolate

Nuts

Berries (like blueberries, strawberries, and blackberries)

Citrus fruits

Kale, spinach, chard and other dark leafy greens (especially in raw form)

Beets

Sweet potatoes

Zucchini and other summer squash

The key is to rotate your foods and not consume the above list in large amounts. You do not usually have to eliminate these foods completely. The most important step to take in the long run is to heal your leaky gut. Your body becomes less reactive to all foods when your digestive system is functioning as it should.

Nightshades and Autoimmune Disease

Nightshades are a family of plants containing chemical compounds called alkaloids. These alkaloid compounds include solanine, nicotine, and capsaicin; they protect the plant from molds and pests and other predators. In humans they can trigger an inflammatory response, particularly in the joints. It's a good idea to avoid them if you have joint pain and see if it makes a difference.

Nightshade Foods

Tomatoes

White potatoes (watch for potato starch on labels)

Eggplant

Okra

Peppers

Goji berries

Tomatillos

Sorrel

Gooseberries

Ground cherries

Pepino melons

Paprika

Cayenne pepper

If your joint pain disappears after eliminating these foods, you might be able to reduce the levels of inflammatory alkaloid compounds by preparing nightshades carefully:

- Peel all potatoes

- Avoid green tomatoes and other unripe nightshades

- Cook nightshade vegetables to further reduce the alkaloid content

Histamine Intolerance

If you have frequent headaches, facial flushing when you drink wine, unexplained anxiety, irregular menstrual cycles, or get an itchy tongue sometimes after you eat, you might have an intolerance to histamine.

Histamine is a compound released by cells in allergic and inflammatory reactions from your immune system. It acts as a neurotransmitter for the brain and is important for the proper digestion of your food. If you don't break histamine down properly, you can develop a sensitivity or intolerance to it.

Common symptoms of histamine intolerance

Headaches
Sleep issues
Hypertension
Vertigo or dizziness
Heart rate variability
Trouble with body temperature regulation
Anxiety
Nausea, vomiting
Abdominal cramps
Flushing
Nasal congestion
Sneezing and watery eyes
Irregular menstrual cycle
Hives
Fatigue
Tissue swelling

Causes of Histamine Intolerance

Leaky gut
Diamine Oxidase (DAO) deficiency
Genetics
Small Intestinal Bacterial Overgrowth (SIBO)
Allergies
Foods high in histamine

Foods High in Histamine

Fermented foods and drinks (including alcohol and kombucha)
Vinegar
Cured meats
Dried fruit
Most citrus fruits
Aged cheese including goat cheese
Walnuts, cashews, and peanuts
Avocados, eggplant, spinach, and tomatoes
Smoked fish
Shellfish
Mackerel, mahi-mahi, tuna, anchovies, sardines
Bananas
Chocolate
Cow's Milk
Papaya, strawberries and pineapple
Wheat Germ
Many artificial preservatives and dyes
Energy drinks
Black, green and mate tea

The key to reducing histamine levels in your diet is to eat everything as fresh as possible. Focus on freshly cooked meats, freshly caught fish, pastured eggs, fresh fruits (that are not high in histamine), fresh vegetables (that are not high in histamine), freshly made nut and seed milks (that are not high in histamine), non-rancid olive and coconut oil, fresh herbs, herbal teas.

If you find histamine is an issue for you, adding a DAO supplement to each meal can help your symptoms resolve if the issue is with DAO (usually because of genetics).

Again, test rather than guess. I do genetic testing to look for issues with DAO in my patients.

Treating the root cause is the way out of histamine intolerance. This means fixing any gut dysbiosis, healing leaky gut, and implementing epigenetic* lifestyle changes to make your body less reactive.

Trouble with Tyramine

Tyramine is an amino acid found in both the body and in protein-containing foods that helps to regulate your blood pressure. Any antibiotic containing linezolid, antidepressants that inhibit monoamine oxidase (MAO) activity, genetic issues with the MAO genes, and foods high in tyramine can all cause high blood pressure, heart palpitations, nausea, and migraine headaches.

As food ages, tyramine levels increase. When I am helping my patients reduce their tyramine levels because of a genetic problem, high blood pressure, or frequent migraines, I tell them to eat food that is as fresh as possible. Any food that is aged, fermented, cured, smoked, old, or left-over from the day before ought to be avoided

when you are experimenting to see if tyramine is an issue. For example, when you bring bananas home that have green tops, they are low in tyramine. When those same bananas begin to form brown spots, they are now loaded with tyramine. The same goes for avocados. So when you see a list of foods high in tyramine, bananas and avocados will be included. However, you can eat them if they are still firm, fresh, and free of brown spots.

High Tyramine Foods

Aged cheeses
Cured or smoked meats or fish, such as
    sausage or salami
Alcohol
Overripe fruits and vegetables
Soy products like miso soup, bean curd,
    or tofu
Fava beans
Soy sauce, teriyaki sauce, or
    bouillon-based sauces
Pickled products like sauerkraut
Sourdough breads
Anchovies
Spoiled food
Nut Butters
Tea and coffee
Processed foods

Like I have said in the other sections of this book, the key is not to be overwhelmed with all of the foods you can't eat. If you have a lot of foods you are reactive to, it just means you have leaky gut and need to focus on healing it—not just from a food standpoint, but also from the place in your mind and body that feels distressed and overwhelmed by all of the foods you "can't

---

*Epigenetics is the study of how your genes are read by your cells, which in turn impacts how they are expressed. In other words, your lifestyle choices can cause your genes to be expressed or to be silent. Your genetics make you unique, and although they are heritable, their expression is not set in stone. You can think of your life as a book. Your cells are the characters in the book. Your DNA is the story arc or plot that provides the characters with instructions for what roles they play. The DNA sequence is the words the characters say. The chapters in the book consist of events that take place in the genes and how they express themselves in your life. Epigenetics is analogous to the author of the book. Several authors can write about the same subject material and each book will be completely different. The overall concept of genetics is like the library where the books are stored.

have." Going into fight-or-flight, feeling trapped and betrayed by your body, the need to "do it perfectly"—these are all mental traps that perpetuate leaky gut. These thoughts and feelings sustain your vicious cycle of alarm, cortisol release from your adrenal glands, and so breakdown your gut wall by the cortisol. They create reactivity in your immune system that matches the reactivity of your mind. Conversely, we are rehabilitating your trigger-happy, gun-slinging immune system into a sweet, tolerant, and even friendly immune system who asks questions before attacking bad guys.

Approaching all of this with a spirit of curiosity and softness allows your body to follow your mind's example of resilience. Your immune system is a mirror of your nervous system, which is only triggered by your perceptions of your experiences in life. If you want to fully heal, you must focus first on the way you perceive your life and the part you play in it.

CHAPTER FIVE

Ayurveda and Eating for Your Body Type

yurveda says we are a microcosm of the macrocosm of the universe, meaning that each element that occurs in nature is also within us. A great way to get to know your body and the feedback it is always trying to communicate to you is through the lens of Ayurvedic medicine. This book is not about Ayurveda. However, Ayurvedic medicine provides an elegant and easy-to-use framework for understanding your body and its feedback. For this reason, I use its principles in my practice.

Ayurveda, a Brief Overview

Long ago the seers of India observed that each human is different. We are not all the same, and therefore there is no one-size-fits-all diet, supplement, or protocol for every person. To put the pieces of your food puzzle together, you need to know what makes you unique. This is a game changer when solving your weight, mood, inflammation, autoimmune, or cancer puzzle. It explains why your friend lost weight on a food plan and you didn't. It helps you to understand that you are not broken, a train wreck, beyond salvation, or any of the other gloom-and-doom self-descriptions I hear from some of my patients who have worked with multiple doctors and tried many plans, only to

remain in misery. Ayurveda understood this 10,000 years ago. You could say that ancient Ayurvedic seers invented personalized medicine.

Your body is an amazingly intelligent and finely engineered vehicle for your spirit. Like the car that carries you around, your body also has a dashboard with feedback gauges. Perhaps you have not learned to read them yet. We are attuned to blood pressure readings, eye exams, and measuring body weight on a scale. However, there is so much more to know about your body. I would like to help you understand the basic feedback mechanisms your body uses. So let's dive in.

The Three Body Types or Doshas

The doshas, or body types, are known as vata, pitta, and kapha. Every person is composed of a ratio of all three doshas determined at the time of conception. When the doshas are in balance, they support the normal functioning of the body; when out of balance, they create disease as they manifest in the layers of the body. Understanding the doshas is key to understanding the uniqueness of each individual in the Ayurvedic paradigm.

Note that not only do we each have different *doshas*, but we also live dosha-specific cycles of life, in dosha-specific climates, eating at dosha-specific times of day. This understanding is all part of the owner's manual Ayurveda offers for how to feed and take care of your beautiful body you were born with.

Vata

Vata is known as "king of the doshas," because when imbalanced, it can quickly imbalance the rest of the doshas. Vata is made of ether and air, and a person with a vata-predominate dosha can have the following characteristics:

- Thin body frame
- Thin lips and hair
- Dry skin and brittle nails
- Cold hands and feet
- Creaky joints
- Learns quickly and forgets quickly
- Walks and talks fast
- Restless and scattered in mind and body
- Imaginative and creative
- Anxious and fearful
- Trouble with sleep
- Constipation
- Difficulty "staying the course" and being consistent (butterfly mind)
- Subject to mood swings

Pitta

A pitta person is the typical "type A personality" because of characteristics engendered by the predominance of fire and water elements. A person with a pitta-predominate dosha can have the following characteristics:

- Medium body frame
- Fair skin, often with freckles or moles and sensitive to the sun
- Strong appetite and digestive fire
- Warm constitution
- Early greying or baldness
- Sharp intelligence and understanding, and a curious mind
- Prone to acne, rashes, sensitive teeth, heartburn, acidity, strong body odor
- Prone to inflammation, irritability (especially in the heat or when meals are skipped), and judgement of self, which can leak out onto others

Kapha

The kapha-predominate person could be called the "cookie baking mom or dad." Kapha is comprised of water and earth, which lends to the loyal stability they offer in relationships. Other characteristics can be:

- Larger body frame with smooth, oily skin and hair

- Grounded, with slower speech and gait

- Cold skin and slow digestion

- Lubricated joints

- Learns slowly but never forgets

- Slow to get going but strong endurance

- Thick hair, nails, and skin

- Gentle and caring with a tendency toward excess weight and fat

- Copious mucus and congestion

- Prone to boils and cysts

- Sugar and salt cravings, poor carbohydrate metabolism, and frequent edema

- Sedentary lifestyle

- Attachments to love and relationships

This is a simplified overview of the 3 doshas. The best way to know your own birth mix of these doshas is to have someone skilled in Ayurvedic pulse diagnosis read your pulse. A more readily available way is to take a dosha assessment or quiz. *You can download one I use on my website at DrKeesha.com free of charge.* These assessments are not 100% accurate, because many times people answer the questions according to how they feel in the moment they are taking the quiz. This only tests your dosha imbalance of the present moment. Think back to how you "usually behave" or how you would have responded at the age of 20. Another option is to have someone who knows you well answer the questions according to what they observe in you.

Knowing your dosha balance from birth and where it is today is a great start towards breaking free of imbalance and disease. It becomes a guide for individualizing your food and lifestyle changes.

There are also feedback mechanisms your body gives you to indicate your level of balance. Here are some quick indicators from Ayurveda to check your own dashboard to see how your body is doing.

Reading the Signs from Your Body

Your Tongue

What is your tongue trying to tell you? It is talking to you if it has anything besides a thin layer of saliva coating it. Your tongue should be pink, smooth, and coated with saliva only. Ancient Ayurvedic seers called rishis outlined many ways to read the body. The tongue's map is as follows:

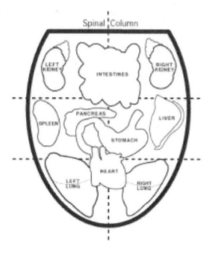

Notice where the various organs of the body are represented on the tongue's surface. If you have a coating in any of these areas, it is a sign of congestion or toxicity (called ama) in or around that organ. If your tongue is scalloped around the edges, it could mean you are not absorbing your nutrients well. If it quivers at the end when you stick it all the way out your thyroid could be imbalanced. A dry, cracked tongue can mean you have a vata imbalance. A bright, red tip can indicate a heart problem.

Checking your tongue twice a day, as you scrape it with a tongue scraper and brush your teeth, gives you feedback for further exploration. Your mouth is the first part of your digestive system. What your tongue looks like is indicative of the health of your entire digestive tract. Keeping tabs on your digestion is the same as keeping tabs on your health.

Your Bowel Movements

I always ask my patients what their bowel movements look like. I often get answers such as, "I never look; I just flush," or "Yuck!" Like it or not, your stools are another feedback feature of your body. You need to be looking before you flush. Check the color, shape, size, frequency, odor, and consistency of your bowel movements. What you want to see in the toilet is a brown, banana-shaped stool that is easy to wipe after, has little odor, and doesn't stick to the toilet. Ideally, it is eliminated in the morning regardless of what you have eaten.

If you have mucous, blood, un-digested food, dry stools, watery or loose stools, infrequent or frequent stools, this is feedback that can trigger you to search further for the cause.

Your Urine

Your urine is a product of your kidneys filtering your toxins. Your urine ought to be about 1½ liters per day, pale yellow, infrequent, and passed without pain or urgency. If you have darker urine, you might be dehydrated. If you have cloudy urine, you could have an infection. Urine with an abnormal color or odor or accompanying pain is feedback from your body. Pay attention; you ignore it at your own risk. If you have an imbalance, it will move from one layer of tissue to another the longer you ignore it.

Pale: anemia

Black: unabsorbed iron or fungus, yeast

Blue: weak heart and lungs/central cynosis

yellow: jaundice

Green: bile regurgitation

Red: pitta in rakta & rassa hyper metabolism

Upper scoliosis

Neck pain

Stress, back pain

Shoulder blade tightness

Lower back ache

Cancer, ulcer or grinding teeth lacerations

Your Sweat

When you exercise, you ought to sweat. Your skin is the largest organ of detoxification you have. It's important that you use it by sweating each day to rid yourself of unwanted toxins and pollutants. However, your sweat is not supposed to have a strong odor. While you might not smell like roses after a long hike, you will also not offend the people around you with your smell if you are healthy. Strong body odor can be a sign of toxicity. A lack of sweat can indicate adrenal fatigue. An abundance of perspiration means your adrenal glands are revved up too high and you are on your way to adrenal fatigue.

Your Hair and Nails

Your hair and nails are another feedback mechanism. What is normal for you will be in accord with your dosha mix. Vata hair is thinner and finer, pitta hair can have a reddish tint to it and appear wavy or curly. Kapha hair will be lustrous and thick. Anything outside of your dosha type's "normal" will be abnormal for you.

For example, when a kapha woman is in my office telling me she is losing too much hair, I need to listen even though her hair might appear thick to me. If a man comes in wanting to talk about what he considers premature balding, if he is a pitta dosha type, I need to address a potential imbalance of his dosha. Pitta people are at risk for premature greying and balding. However, male pattern baldness can also signal too much testosterone for men or women. Loss of hair that feels like straw and is dry to the touch can reflect thyroid and adrenal imbalance. On the other hand, hair falling out in chunks can mean you have parasites in your gut. Greasy hair might indicate you have a kapha imbalance.

The same rule of "normal for the dosha type" is true for fingernails. Vata nails are thinner and more brittle. Pitta nails are soft and pink, and Kapha nails are thick and strong.

Your fingernails ought to have a half moon at the cuticle or base of the nail on each finger. They should look and feel smooth rather than rough or ridged. White spots can indicate a zinc or calcium deficiency. Pale nails can be a red flag for anemia, while a yellow nail is a sign of a liver imbalance. Blue nails usually signal heart or lung problems.

Your Skin

Skin is one of the first places an imbalance will show up. Do not ignore the signs on your skin. Each of us has skin that is typical and healthy for our dosha type. Vata people can have thinner, dryer skin that is prone to wrinkles as they age. Pitta folks have skin that is at risk for inflammation. Their skin will be more likely to have moles and freckles, burn easily and break out more readily. Kapha skin is thicker, oilier, and can be prone to cysts and boils.

Antibiotics do not treat the root cause of acne. If you have an inflammatory issue such as acne, rosacea, psoriasis, or eczema, think digestive imbalance rather than topical skin-care products. Leaky gut, intestinal permeability, is the root cause for autoimmune disease, including autoimmune issues of the skin such as psoriasis and eczema. Intestinal permeability or leaky gut is a disruption in the lining of the intestinal wall. This allows undigested food molecules to escape into the body where the immune system fights against them as if they were a virus or bacteria.

Leaky gut is the root cause for many diseases. One of the first places it shows up is on the tongue and on the skin. Pay attention to the feedback your body is giving you so it doesn't have to turn up the volume and scream to be heard.

Your Facial Lines

Hopefully this discussion serves to raise your awareness of the signs your body sends you when it's out of balance. You can head out of balance for any number of reasons:

- When the weather changes.
- If you don't get enough sleep or too much sleep.
- If you don't eat right for your body type.
- If you are having mental or emotional stress.
- With aging.
- If you don't hydrate properly.
- If you exercise at the wrong time of day or in a way that doesn't match your body type.

Your body is constantly attempting to stay in balance, but if you don't pay attention, if might get so far out of balance that it's hard to come back. Ultimately, this can result in chronic or acute disease.

The 6 Stages of Disease Progression

Ayurvedic medicine teaches us that we have 7 tissue layers, or dhatus. Healthy tissues are created by the proper digestion of our foods, thoughts, and emotions. If you are not properly digesting or are not making nutritious choices for your individual body type, there are serious consequences: First, your digestive fire, or agni, will not be healthy enough for the formation of your dhatus, or tissue layers. Second, there will be a build-up of toxicity, or ama. Third, you will not have the ojas, or vital essence you need to live an energy filled life. And fourth, an imbalanced dosha will move from its place of origin to a place of weakness in the body and create further imbalance and eventually disease.

There are 6 stages of disease progression as the body becomes more and more imbalanced. The 6 stages of disease are:

Stage 1: Accumulation
Stage 2: Aggravation
Stage 3: Dissemination
Stage 4: Localization
Stage 5: Manifestation
Stage 6: Disruption

It is said that in our culture we do not usually notice or pay attention to our imbalance until it has progressed to full blown disease, stage 4 or 5, when our forward motion and productivity are impaired. I know this was true for me, and I see it every day in my medical practice. The fast-paced, productivity-oriented society we live in has us so out of touch with our bodies and minds, we do not notice the first signs of imbalance, and for that, we pay the price.

CHAPTER SIX

Ayurveda and the Six Tastes

The Six Tastes and Your Emotions

I want to invite you to explore your relationship with food through the lens of Ayurveda for a moment. Ayurveda teaches that all food can be categorized into six tastes: sweet, salty, bitter, astringent, sour, and pungent. As you can see, sweet is only 1/6th of the taste palate. We have receptors on our tongues for all six tastes. Yet, we Americans seem to crave sweet and have a distaste for bitter and astringent.

Several years ago, while I was deeply immersed in my Ayurvedic training and studies, I found myself in the grocery store thinking about the different tastes of the foods I was buying. I realized that the standard American diet, the SAD diet, emphasized mostly the sweet and salty tastes.

As I was reaching into the freezer for a bag of frozen organic blueberries, a thought struck me squarely between the eyes. This realization was so profoundly life changing for me that the imagery has never left me. I realized the six tastes Ayurveda used to classify food can also be used to classify thoughts, feelings, and experiences, which you now know also have to be digested in a healthy way or you will not be nourished by them. I saw clearly that the typical American craved the taste that brought comfort from childhood, which was tied to pleasant emotional experiences. Allow me explain.

Industrialized cultures have embraced the time savings promised by "convenience foods." We even call them "fast foods." Convenience foods and fast foods are loaded with salt and sugar. If you have grown up on these so-called foods, your palate will be trained to detect those tastes and judge them as "good" or "comforting." If you grew up on kale, broccoli, cauliflower, chard, parsley, cilantro, dandelion greens, and other bitter and astringent foods, your palate will be attuned to these tastes and judge them as good, and even comforting perhaps.

Industrialized countries like the United States have also come to rely on certain material comforts and a standard of life that doesn't get swept away when a storm blows in. In fact, when we do get a destructive storm, it's experienced not as just a natural disaster, but a life-changing catastrophe that threatens the trust and faith we have for our safety, which the great majority of Americans never question.

Contrast this to countries like Bangladesh, listed the happiest country in the world in 2009 when I was mulling this over in my head in the grocery store. At that time, the United States was ranked 46th in the world happiness survey. The economy was strong. There were still jobs to go to. Healthy babies were being born. We were experiencing very few natural disasters. Our banking system was still intact and our government was still governing. We had no deadly diseases wiping us out. In short, we had every reason to be happier than the world happiness survey indicated we were.

Now let's take a look at the happiest people on the planet in 2009. Bangladesh is 80% flood plain. It lies between the Bay of Bengal and several of its tributaries and has an extensive sea coastline, and it sits on the Ganges Delta. Every year about 18% of the country is flooded, destroying millions of homes and causing the loss of life to over 5,000 people. During the monsoon season, in excess of 75% of the country can be flooded in any given year. This causes loss of life, livelihood, and homes. Devastation on that level is unimaginable to Americans. Yet, these people who are at the mercy of Mother Nature each and every year are the happiest of all the people on the planet? Why?

Well, that was my big epiphany. They do not feel entitled. They are filled with appreciation and gratitude for what they have and are joyfully present with the times of good fortune and loving community. They are focused on what is sweet in their lives, but not attached to it in an entitled way. They understand and are perhaps even more comfortable with bitter, sour, and astringent experiences than we are. As a nation, they expect to encounter challenges they cannot foresee or control. I think this is fascinating, and is certainly relevant to the rise of autoimmunity in our culture. We Americans expect sweetness from our lives, and if we don't get it (and maybe even if we do), we seek it out in the form of food.

Let's say you have a hard day at work or at home with someone you are caring

for. What do you wish for? Perhaps, some form of sweet taste or experience to make up for the shortfall of your day in its quotient of sweetness that you were expecting? If you're like many I know, you might reach for a sweet fruit, a cookie, some potato chips, and then want to sit and take in something that brings you sweet pleasure on the television, computer, or your electronic reader. Whatever brings you pleasure could be considered the same as a sweet taste. It's going to act the same in your body. Too much of it will make you fat.

If you are sad, you are experiencing a salty experience. If you are angry, you are experiencing a pungent experience. Pungent foods are hot like chili peppers. Bitterness can arise in you when you feel betrayed and feel resentful. This is the bitter taste, which includes foods such as kale, broccoli, and green leafy vegetables. If you have an interaction that leaves a "sour taste in your mouth," you have just experienced a sour experience. Foods that are sour include lemons, limes, and dill pickles. And lastly, any experience that makes you "pucker up" due to fear and anxiety is an astringent experience. Foods that are astringent are green apples, tea, and pomegranates.

It seemed to me, as I was reflecting that day long ago in the grocery store, holding a thawing bag of blueberries in my hand, that we Americans need to build up our resilience for life experiences that include something other than happy and sad. We needed to expand our palates and become more sophisticated in skills for handling all six tastes and all six kinds of experiences. This would be good for our digestive system on a physical level as well as on a mental and emotional level. After all, how many people in Bangladesh are taking anti-depressants compared to people in the United States? If the world happiness survey is any indication, there is a large disparity between the two populations. What does the diet in Bangladesh consist of? All six tastes of course.

The six tastes all impact your dosha balance. As you can now see, it's very important to tune into the taste of your food, your experiences, and your life. Rasa, the Sanskrit word for taste, also means experience, enthusiasm, essence, and juice. So taste is a reflection of your enthusiasm for your life and reflects as well your physical health and state of mind. The Ayurvedic concept of rasa determines not only your experience of food, but even the flavor of your life and experiences. It may seem a surprise to many, but taste is an element of the physical realm that can bridge and unite the body, mind, heart, and spirit.

Remember also that in the Ayurvedic paradigm, you are composed of five elements—earth, water, fire, air, and space (ether). The six tastes also contain all five elements. And like the doshas, each taste is composed of primarily two elements each.

The 6 Tastes of Ayurveda and Your Perceptions

Foods	Taste	Emotions
	Sweet	Happiness, joy, contentment, satisfaction.
	Sour	Having an interaction with someone that leaves "a sour taste in your mouth".
	Pungent	Anger, annoyance and frustration.
	Astringent	Fear, worry and anxiety.
	Bitter	Betrayal, hurt, resentment and unforgiveness.
	Salty	Sadness, grief and loss.

Dr. Keesha

The 6 Tastes and Their Primary Elements

Sweet: Earth & Water
Sour: Earth & Fire
Salty: Water & Fire
Pungent: Fire & Air
Bitter: Air & Space
Astringent: Air & Earth

Each of the six tastes then has an effect on each dosha, (either pacifying or aggravating), temperature (either heating or cooling), post-digestive effect (either predictable or unpredictable), each organ and tissue, the direction of movement within the body, and the emotional impact. Your tongue has taste receptors on it (see Figure 5), but so does your mind.

As is always the case with Ayurveda, the impact of the six tastes will fluctuate with your age, dosha balance, and environmental factors such as time of day, climate, and season. The key is to listen to the feedback your body gives you. Stay attuned to the subtle fluctuations of your body's response to what you are tasting, and you will begin to speak its language and have more skill in communicating with it in a collaborative way.

Let's take a look at each taste.

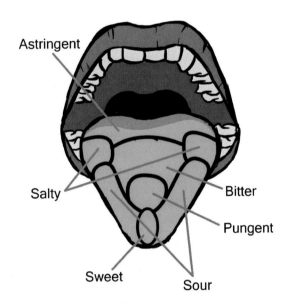

Figure 5: **Balancing the Doshas Through the Six Tastes**

	Most Balancing	Most Aggravating
Vata	Sweet, Sour, Salty	Bitter, Pungent, Astringent
Pitta	Sweet, Bitter, Astringent	Sour, Salty, Pungent
Kapha	Pungent, Bitter, Astringent	Sweet, Sour, Salty

In the summary of the 6 Tastes below, the minus sign (-) after the dosha indicates a balancing (decreasing) effect on that dosha, while a plus sign (+) indicates an aggravating (increasing) effect.

The Sweet Taste and the Doshas

The sweet taste is the flavor of sugars such as fructose, lactose, glucose, sucrose and maltose. The sweet taste is provided by eating carbohydrates, fats and proteins. Sweet is not necessarily candy and baked goods. It's also quite subtle, such as the sweet taste in grains. People do not usually think of corn as dessert. Here's how the sweet taste registers with your system.

V- P- K+: Balances vata and pitta; aggravates kapha.
Qualities: Heavy, cold, oily, soft, grounding, building, and not easy to digest
Emotions when consumed in balance: Generosity, love, compassion, bliss, and happiness
Emotions when consumed in excess: Possessiveness, attachment, and greed
Organs affected: Lungs and thyroid
Tissues affected: All 7 layers or dhatus

Examples of sweet foods:
Fruit: Melons, bananas, dried fruit, dates, mangos, and figs
Vegetables: Cooked carrots, sweet potatoes, butternut squash, acorn squash, beets, and olives
Grains: Wheat, corn, quinoa, and rice
Legumes: Lentils, mung beans, navy beans, and garbanzo beans
Nuts & Seeds: Pumpkin seeds, almonds, cashews, and coconut
Dairy & Eggs: All kinds of animal and seed and grain milks, eggs, and ghee

Meat: Salmon, beef, bison, the dark meat on chicken, and pork
Sweeteners: All of them
Spices: Vanilla bean, saffron, cinnamon, cardamom, coriander, mint, fennel, tarragon, basil, bay leaf, and caraway

Just enough sweet builds ojas; too much causes weight gain, lethargy, and inflammation. It will cause a kapha imbalance if over indulged in.

The Sour Taste and the Doshas

The sour taste is the result of the presence of acids such as oxalic acid, malic acid, citric acid, lactic acid, and ascorbic acid in our food choices. These acids generate the release of saliva to encourage efficient digestion.

V- P+ K+: Balances vata; aggravates pitta and kapha
Qualities: Hot, oily, liquid, and light
Emotions when consumed in balance: Understanding, appreciation, comprehension, and discrimination
Emotions when consumed in excess: Hate, selfishness, agitation, jealousy, hyperactivity, criticism, jealousy, and rejection
Organs affected: The lungs
Tissues affected: All of the dhatus except the reproductive system

Examples of sour foods:
Fruit: Lime, lemon, grapefruit, and grapes
Vegetables: Tomatoes and pickled and fermented foods (including alcohol and vinegar)
Grains: Yeast breads
Dairy & Eggs: Yogurt, butter, sour cream, and cheese
Spices: Garlic

The sour taste is essential for proper digestion and most sour foods have anti-oxidant properties. Too much can cause or exacerbate inflammatory skin conditions such as psoriasis and eczema. It can also cause tooth and gum sensitivity and be very drying.

The Salty Taste and the Doshas

Salt is present in sea water and is essential for life. The earliest known use of salt as a seasoning and method of food preservation dates back to 8,000 years ago. Salt was a treasured commodity used in trade by the ancient Egyptians, Hebrews, Greeks, Romans, Indians, Hittites, and Byzantines. Salt is now obtained from seawater and mineral rich springs and sold as sea salt and table salt and is present in many processed foods.

V- P+ K+: Balances vata; aggravates pitta and kapha
Qualities: Oily, hot and heavy
Emotions when consumed in balance: Enthusiasm, interest, courage, and confidence
Emotions when consumed in Excess: Addiction, attachment, greed, irritability, temptation, and irritability
Organs affected: The kidneys
Tissues affected: The nervous system, blood, fat, and muscle

Examples of salty foods:
Fruit: None
Vegetables: sea vegetables and celery
Dairy & Eggs: Cottage cheese
Meat & Fish: Tuna
Spices: Mineral, table, sea, and rock salt, soy sauce and tamari

The salty taste aids in digestion, maintains electrolyte and fluid balance,

and energizes the tissues it affects. Too much of it can cause water retention, high blood pressure, causes loss and greying of hair, and can increase the acidity and inflammation of the body.

The Pungent Taste and the Doshas

Onions, garlic, scallions, chives and leeks are known as "the five pungent spices" and are forbidden in many meditative spiritual traditions because they are said to raise the heat of anger and passion, which is thought to interfere with the goal of reaching samadhi (union with the Divine).

V+ P+ K-: Balances kapha; aggravates pitta and vata.
Qualities: Light, hot, dry, aromatic, and sharp
Emotions when consumed in balance: Curiosity, clarity, vitality, vigor, enthusiasm, and excitement
Emotions when consumed in excess: Irritation, anger, aggression, rage, envy, and competitiveness
Organs affected: The heart and stomach
Tissues affected: The reproductive system and the blood

Examples of pungent foods:
Fruit: None
Vegetables: Garlic, onions, leeks, shallots, radishes, mustard greens, raw spinach, kohlrabi, turnips and chilies
Grains: Spelt and buckwheat
Nuts & Seeds: Mustard seeds
Spices: Most spices, but especially cumin, cayenne, ginger, black pepper, cardamom, cloves, hing, and paprika

The pungent taste fires up your digestive juices, or agni. It helps to eliminate ama and mucous and aids in detoxification, especially via sweating. Too much can cause insomnia, inflammation, digestive reflux, hemorrhoids, constipation, and ulcerations.

The Bitter Taste and the Doshas

Bitter is a protective mechanism used by some species of the plant kingdom to discourage animals from eating them. Bitter can be toxic and even poisonous. Bitterness is a subject of interest to researchers who study evolution because the ability to taste bitter can be life-saving. It is thought that the overconsumption of sweet has dulled the ability for some people to be able to sense the bitter taste.

V+ P- K-: Balances pitta and kapha; aggravates vata
Qualities: Dry, light, and cold
Emotions when consumed in balance: Self-awareness, detachment, introspection, and clarity
Emotions when consumed in excess: Separation, loneliness, boredom, cynicism, rejection, and isolation
Organs affected: The spleen, liver and pancreas
Tissues affected: The nervous system, reproductive system, blood and fat

Examples of bitter foods:

Fruit: none
Vegetables: Dark leafy greens, Jerusalem artichokes, eggplant, burdock root, and bitter melon
Nuts and Seeds: Sesame seeds and oil, coffee beans, cocoa bean
Spices: Turmeric, dill, fenugreek, saffron, and cumin

The bitter taste is a powerful detoxifier. It also serves as an appetite stimulant,

muscle and skin toner, gas reliever, and digestive aid. In excess it is drying and can aggravate bone loss, constipation, nausea, and dizziness.

The Astringent Taste and the Doshas

The astringent taste is most often produced by tannins in the leaves, bark, and outer skins of fruits and trees. It is the least common of all the 6 tastes and causes you to pucker up when you sense it on your tongue.

V+ P- K-: Balances pitta and kapha; aggravates vata
Qualities: Cold, dry, and heavy
Emotions when consumed in balance: Grounded and stable
Emotions when consumed in excess: Anxiety, fear, depression, rigidity, and resentment
Organs affected: The colon
Tissues affected: The reproductive system, blood, and muscle

Examples of astringent foods:

Fruit: Green bananas, pomegranates, cranberries, and tart apples
Vegetables: Broccoli, cabbage, Brussels sprouts, cauliflower, lettuce, alfalfa sprouts, avocado, raw carrots, green beans, peas, potatoes, and most raw vegetables
Grains: Rye and wheat pasta
Legumes: Most beans
Meat: The white meat on chicken and venison
Spices: Oregano, saffron, rosemary, fennel, parsley, basil, bay leaf, caraway, coriander, dill, marjoram, nutmeg, poppy seeds, vanilla, and tea leaves

The astringent taste helps with blood clotting, decongests, improves absorption, binds the stool, helps keep tissues held together, and scrapes fat. Too much can lower libido, cause gas, bloating, and constipation, a dry mouth, and paralysis.

Using Food and Spice Therapeutically

Considering the information above, you can see that in order to reduce kapha, it would be helpful to eat pungent foods like onions, radishes, ginger, and cumin. Items such as green leafy vegetables and turmeric and astringent foods, including broccoli and cabbage, would also serve to reduce the extra fluid, mucous, and body weight that can be a common imbalance of a kapha individual. Eating sweets just aggravates kapha, which can cause this very same excess mucous, fluid build-up, and weight gain.

A pitta person who is feeling irritable can focus on foods that are sweet, bitter, or astringent. Again, sweet does not mean cookies and candy but rather fruit and sweet vegetables like yams. Herbs and spices can also be used instead of food.

Ayurvedic medicine uses the tastes in spices therapeutically to bring the body and mind into balance. In the following table you will see some examples of spices and how they impact the balance of the doshas. A negative (-) sign before the letter means it reduces that dosha and a plus (+) sign means it increases the dosha. V stands for vata, P for pitta and K for kapha. On pages 107–109 I have given you some spice, or churna, mixtures you can play with to bring your own constitution into balance.

Spice	Effect on the Doshas
Aniseed	-V, K +P
Asafoetida (Hing)	-V, K +P
Black Pepper	-V, K +P
Caraway	-V, K +P
Cardamom	-V, K +P
Chili	-V, K +P
Cinnamon	-V, K +P
Clove	-V +P
Coriander	-P, K
Cumin	-VPK
Dill Seed	-V, K +P
Fennel Seed	-V, K +P
Fenugreek	-V, K +P
Garlic	-V, K +P
Mace	-K +P
Mustard Seed	-V, K +P
Nutmeg	-VPK
Onion Seed	-P
Poppy Seed	-V +K
Saffron	-VPK
Sesame Seed	-V, P +K
Star Anise	-VPK
Turmeric	-VK

CHAPTER SEVEN

Swapping Toxic for Terrific

Going from fatigued to energized is a process. It's not usually one thing that creates an autoimmune disease, hormone havoc, or cancer. It's not normally one food or one habit that causes you to gain weight or experience pain. Likewise, it's not just one thing that's going to get you to optimal health.

Energy is created at a cellular level. There are many habits, foods, and lifestyle choices that affect the way your cells reproduce and make energy for you. Some of these habits are thought habits and some of them are dietary. Most of them you can control if you know what to look for.

I wrote this book for that very reason. I didn't know what caused my autoimmune disease when I was diagnosed. It turns out I had several food sensitivities I was unaware of that were causing me to gain weight, have joint inflammation and pain, and suck my energy dry. I didn't know why I was so tired all of the time. I just wanted "my old self back." Have you ever felt like that?

Well, my old self was not what I got. I actually got an upgraded model of myself once I learned what the pieces of the puzzle were that were creating my autoimmunity. When I was diagnosed with rheumatoid arthritis, I was told it was just a matter of time before I got worse and had to go on immune-modulating drugs because I had a grandfather with rheumatoid arthritis.

You are not a victim of your genetics. After one year of avoiding specific foods and thoughts, and healing past trauma, I reversed my autoimmunity. It has not come back in 23 years.

It was not easy implementing the epigenetic lifestyle modifications to my diet and my thoughts that were required to reverse my autoimmunity. However, I wouldn't trade the journey I have been on. I now look at illness and pain as the gifts that woke me up. I now understand that beliefs, thoughts, emotions, genetics, toxins, infections, digestive health, and food choices are all part of the puzzle.

Epigenetic Hacks for a Healthier You

As I have mentioned, not all things we call food are great for you. Did you know that there are more than 3,000 chemicals added to your food supply? These are commonly called food additives, and they definitely play havoc on hormone levels, libido, weight, mood, energy, your immune and digestive systems, and therefore your overall health.

There are also hundreds of thousands of additional toxins we pollute our brain with every year. I'm talking about thoughts and feelings that make us feel fearful, anxious, guilty, or ashamed. Yes, these too make us feel distinctly "sick," and they alter our hormone levels. This is something

Ayurvedic medicine recognized millennia ago: we ingest more than food and drink. We also ingest thoughts and emotions, which, once digested, become part of our bodies.

If those thoughts are positive and progressive, they boost our vitality; if they are negative, they drain us. In this book, we'll look at both the physical and nonphysical dimensions of what we "eat" that impact your hormones, your immune system, and your energy level.

You might wonder what exactly a hormone IS and DOES and why you should bother reading about "hormone hacks." A hormone signals the cells in the body so they know what to do next. These little messenger chemicals are the important regulators of your mood, your sex drive, your weight, your menstrual cycle (if you have one), your skin complexion, your energy, your sleep, your appetite and food cravings, your memory, and so on. So let's move on to what's hijacking them and give you some hormone-happy swaps. The road to inflammation is paved with the following 21 toxic chemicals, foods, and thoughts.

Seven Chemical Hormone and Immune Disruptor Swaps

In the United States, it's legal to add artificial flavorings, coloring, preservatives, and chemicals to our food supply. Though it's legal, it's definitely not healthy. So if you are eating processed foods, please pay careful attention to this section. If you are one of those rare souls who never eat out of a bag, can, or package, you are likely not eating the "sinful seven" and can skip down to the next sections: Seven Food Hormone Disruptors and Energy Drains, and Seven Mental Hormone and Immune Disruptors.

1. Artificial Sweeteners

Did you know that eating artificial sweeteners actually increases your appetite and your cravings for sweet tastes? When it comes to your weight, it's not all about calories. Aspartame is one of the worst offenders. In 1984 when I was in college, I wrote an investigative report for school on aspartame. I had to dig through microfiches in the library in those days for the data and press reports. My paper exposed the fraudulent way this product was pushed through the FDA and the impact it would have on U.S. citizens. At the time, I predicted that Aspartame would soon be pulled from shelves. All of the damning information I had to dig for back then is now widely available with a keystroke thanks to the Internet, and yet aspartame is still in our food supply.

We have an exploding "diabesity" (diabetes + obesity) problem in the United States. This is largely due to our need for the sweet taste in food, drinks, and junk food, which we satisfy with foods containing natural sweeteners and chemical additives like aspartame (Nutrasweet), sucralose, and saccharin. If you ingest such chemicals, you run a high risk of having your hormones disrupted to a point that you can gain weight and create toxicity in your brain.

Did you know sucralose (Splenda) is made from chlorine and can cause leaky gut and make inflammatory bowel disease worse? Leaky gut is common in Americans today because of the number of chemicals being dumped into our food. It is the root cause of asthma, food allergies, chronic sinusitis, eczema, hives, migraines, irritable bowel, fungal disorders, fibromyalgia, and inflammatory joint disorders, including rheumatoid arthritis.

Saccharine has been linked to cancer and yet those little pink Sweet'n Low packets are still on every table in cafes.

We now know that sugar is eight times more addictive than cocaine and is the number one cause of inflammation; and inflammation is the cause of autoimmunity and cancer.

High fructose corn syrup is found in almost any junk food that comes in a package. These packaged junked foods are found in every grocery store and mini-mart across America. But just because they are inexpensive and easy to access does not mean they are good for you. High fructose corn syrup can cause insulin resistance and leaky gut, which you now know leads to diabesity, inflammation, mood problems, hormone imbalance, fatigue, autoimmune diseases, and cancers.

The Swap
Lowering your sugar intake is a good thing. Try coconut palm sugar. It raises your blood sugar at about half the rate of cane sugar and brings a lovely sweet taste to your baking. It's a good bridge towards leaving the need for sweet behind. Once you have gotten yourself off of sugar and its harmful artificial cousins, try using stevia, Lo Han (monk fruit), and xylitol. Be careful with xylitol though. It can cause gut upset like gas, bloating, and diarrhea if you go overboard with it. My family can attest to that!

2. Synthetic Trans Fats
Crackers, many manufactured baked goods, chips, and most fried foods contain partially hydrogenated vegetable oil, which causes inflammation. We now know that all disease is exacerbated by or caused by inflammation.

Synthetic trans fats have been linked to cancer, stroke, diabetes, heart disease, the production of sex hormones, and a decrease in immune function and response. They are definitely on the list of "hormone disruptors" for a good reason.

The Swap
Fat is not the enemy. We have been conditioned by crafty marketing to believe "fat free" is healthy. This is untrue. Use coconut oil, ghee (clarified butter), olive oil, or avocado oil in your cooking. Fish oil, nuts, and seeds help balance your healthy fats with the fats found in animal protein. Animal fats are not bad for you, but your fat ratios are important to balance.

These healthful fats should not be over consumed if you are trying to lose weight or are a kapha body type in the Ayurvedic framework. Contrary to the American rule, "if a little bit is good, a lot must be better," your fat intake should be individualized to your genetics, body type, and current cellular needs.

If you are a vata body type, these fats will help you stay grounded, moisturized, and feeling fabulous. All body types need some healthy fats. Use my recipe later in this book and try your hand at making ghee. It's a wonderful eye moisturizer as well as substitute for butter if you are dairy intolerant.

3. Artificial Flavors
Please realize that the term "artificial flavor" on a label has no meaning. This might mean there is a blend of several hundred additives or just a few. Many of these chemicals are hormone disruptors, which not only make you feel moody and fat, but are also cancer risks.

Did you know that the artificial butter flavoring on microwave popcorn has a chemical that has been shown to trigger Alzheimer's disease? The term "artificial flavoring" (or "natural flavor") on a label can also mean genetically engineered flavor enhancers.

The Swap

Avoid anything artificially or "naturally" flavored. Eat healthy whole foods that taste good because they are good, and good for you. You can, if you wish, also make your own truly natural flavorings to add to your recipes if you desire. Later in this book, I have included some recipes for making your own flavorings that won't cause hormone and immune chaos.

4. Monosodium Glutamate (MSG)

MSG can excite your cells to the point of cell death. That is the meaning of the word *excitotoxin*. MSG is an excitotoxin. Still FDA approved, MSG shows up in Chinese food, flavorings, salad dressings, frozen dinners, junk food, and some meats. It is a hormone disruptor and is linked to Alzheimer's disease, Parkinson's disease, Lou Gehrig's disease, learning disabilities, autoimmunity, and cancer.

The Swap

Put your own spice mixtures together at home where you know exactly what is going into them. On pages 107-109 I have provided taste-popping Ayurvedic spice mixture recipes that will help you reduce inflammation and balance your immune system. No need for MSG!

5. Artificial Coloring

Food manufacturers dump 15 million pounds of artificial dyes into our nation's food supply. There are countless studies indicating their harmful effects on children, ranging from learning disorders to attention and activity disorders. Warning labels on food alert children, pregnant women, and the elderly to stay away. This should be a signal for the rest of us to avoid these harmful chemicals as well.

Food dyes are hormone disruptors and are linked to cancer, allergies, leaky gut, and autoimmunity. Red dye #40 was shown to induce hyperactivity in children and brain tumors in mice. Some of these studies were actually conducted by the chemical industry itself.

When I take groups to Peru, my travel companions get to see how *natural dyes* are made. The people of the Andes use a small fungus that grows on a cactus to color their cloth red. They use plant fibers and matter from their environment to get the brilliant hues that appear in the rich tapestries that brighten every village in the mountains of Peru. Their incidence of cancer and leaky gut and ADHD? It has been nothing compared to the U.S., but sadly it is beginning to rise due to their craze for soda pop (a serious hormone disruptor loaded with artificial dyes).

The Swap

I have been experimenting with natural food dyes in my kitchen, using items I can get locally. Beet juice powder makes a gorgeous red or pink, depending on how much you use. I used it last holiday season in a sugarless icing I made for some paleo cookies for my grandkids. Turmeric makes a lovely yellow. Blueberry juice brings out the purple. Carrot powder creates a popping orange. Liquid chlorophyll turns everything green. Cocoa powder creates a rich earth tone. Try experimenting and find the natural food dyes in your kitchen. It's fun!

6. High Fructose Corn Syrup (HFCS)

High fructose corn syrup is a byproduct of corn silage that this country has way too much of due to a variety of political factors in agribusiness. The solution for disposing of this excess is to make a sugar alternative and dump it into our food supply.

The problem is that HFCS is much worse than even sugar is for the body. It is processed through the liver and can cause liver damage and disrupt hormones the same way other toxicants and alcohol do. It is turned into fat by the liver and is a big contributor to the diabesity problem in our country. One can of soda contains more of this obesity-causing agent than you should consume in a day.

Incidentally, the fructose in fruit must also be watched. Do not consume more than 15 grams of fructose a day. This means no more than $1/3$ cup of raisins or two dates for the whole day. Often I see my patients throwing a lot more than that in their smoothies in the morning. This raises your blood sugar first thing in the morning and can cause a roller coaster of sugar cravings and energy crashes for the rest of the day— leaving you feeling fatigued and frustrated at the end of the ride.

The Swap
If you want your beverages to taste sweet try this:

1) Fill a glass container with water.

2) Slice a few pieces of your favorite fruit into the jar of water.

3) Add a few of your favorite herbs.

4) Drink all day and enjoy this refreshing fruit-tasting water without the inflammation or the sugar.

Some mixtures I love are cucumbers and mint, strawberries and mint, basil and blueberry, watermelon and lemongrass, orange and lemongrass. Fruity, fresh and fast! On page 153 you will find my master recipe template for fruit-infused waters. Get creative and have fun.

7. Preservatives

There are many chemicals used to lengthen the shelf life of food. These are linked to health issues such as cancer, hormone imbalances, hyperactivity in children, memory issues, allergies, autoimmunity, and neurological issues.

The following are some common names you will find on labels at a grocery store near you:

- Sodium benzoate. Found in fruit juices, salad dressings, and soft drinks. Can cause hyperactivity in children.

- Sodium nitrite. Found in lunch and deli meats, bacon, and hotdogs. Can cause stomach, pancreatic, and colorectal cancers.

- Butylated hydroxyanisole. Used in cosmetics, rubber, petroleum products, medications such as statin drugs, and animal feed. Can cause neurological issues, autoimmunity, and cancer.

- Butylated hydroxytoluene. Found in rice, poultry, cosmetics, and medications. Can cause cancer, autoimmunity, and neurological issues.

The Swap

Make your own salad dressings and eat whole foods. Shun shelf life and eat seasonal and regional fresh food as much as you can.

Try my favorite fast and easy salad dressings on page 186.

Instead of chemical preservatives, use your freezer to preserve your food if you want to save both your left-overs and your hormones.

Seven Food Hormone Disruptor and Energy Drain Swaps

1. Sugar

Sugar can definitely make you feel energized—temporarily. It gives you a bump in energy and can feed your brain if you have skipped a meal and are running on empty. The problem is it causes inflammation, addiction, and craving, and can really play havoc with your hormone balance and neurotransmitters (the messenger chemicals from the brain that help you feel good, focus, experience sexual desire, feel motivated, remember, and respond to danger properly).

When I say sugar, I am talking about the white, brown, and liquid forms, as well as your carbohydrate count for the day. The *carbohydrate* count on a food label is really a secret code for sugar content.

Remember this formula: For every 4 grams of carbohydrate you ingest, you are actually eating or drinking 1 teaspoon of sugar.

Make sure you do the math and keep track of your sugar consumption. I hear all day from my patients, "I don't eat sugar." But when I start digging into what they are eating, I find they are not counting bananas, pasta, bread, rice, wine, beer, and so on.

Americans are eating sugar in the form of pastries, candies, cookies, soft drinks, but also as French fries, chips, crackers, breads, cereals, and grains. The great news is today it's easier than ever to cook, bake, and eat without eating more than the allowed 6 teaspoons of sugar per day (24 grams).

Consider: one can of soda has 46 grams of carbohydrates (that's the equivalent of 11+ teaspoons of sugar) plus 44 grams of sugar—for a whopping total of 22 teaspoons of sugar. Bye-bye hormones and hello fat and fatigue!

The Swap

Some replacements for sugar that are easier on your blood sugar balance than maple syrup and honey are stevia, lo han (monk fruit), xylitol, & erythritol (use with caution), coconut palm sugar, and real fruit (in small amounts).

A paleo-style diet encourages us to eat as our ancestors did. Early humans did not have any of the sugar replacements I just listed other than the fruit, and that was eaten in small amounts and only in season.

However, sometimes you just want to celebrate. If you are trying to make a birthday cake or celebrate a family event that requires a special family favorite, experiment with cooking up a "paleo" version. This cookbook gives you master recipe templates to master the art of cooking, baking, and eating in a way that won't agitate your immune system and hormone balance, because it removes common inflammatory triggers like grains, gluten, dairy, sugar, soy, corn, coffee, alcohol, and lectins.

Try these recipes for at least 3 months and keep track of your weight, digestive system, energy level, hormone functions, and quality of sleep. If you have not significantly improved in most of these areas, you likely need functional medicine testing to go a little deeper into root cause for your inflammatory issue.

2. Alcohol

Alcohol is another commonly ingested product that can make you feel unfettered for a short time, and then less than wonderful afterwards. Alcohol affects different people in different ways. If you have a candida or bacterial overgrowth in your gut, beer and wine will make those little critters very very happy. They love it when you drink! They reproduce and then cause inflammation, hormone issues, brain fog, lack of focus, skin break outs, digestive pain, and exacerbate autoimmunity and other imbalances you might have going on.

Depending on your genetics, you may or may not be able to manage alcohol. For certain genetic types, alcohol can trigger Alzheimer's disease, heart disease, inflammation, obesity, and liver disease.

Alcohol can also trigger addiction in the brain and give a false sense of what you need to be social, witty, or relaxed. Booze is dehydrating. It interferes with hormone production and sleep. It's also a huge libido and sexual performance killer.

When I discuss the possibility of leaving alcohol behind for a certain period of time or even for life (if it's a genetic issue), I have patients who get quite upset at the prospect of doing without a nightly cocktail or two, a glass or two of wine with dinner, or drinks with friends.

I have nothing but compassion for you if you feel this way. I know just how hard it is to change a habit and kick an addiction. I am a recovering sugar addict myself. So

here are some ideas I give to my patients when we have this discussion.

The Swap

- When you know you are going to be in a social setting where it will be necessary for you to have a drink in your hand, ask for soda water with a lime or cranberry twist.

- If you are used to having wine with dinner, use the recipes on page 153 and pour from a beautiful crystal decanter filled with water, sliced fruit, and fresh herbs.

- If you drink alcohol to "relax" before bed, switch to my favorite Ayurvedic sleepy-time "cocktail," which actually does relax you and aid in sleep. It's essential to get 7-8 hours of sleep a night. Follow the recipe for restful sleep on page 132.

3. Fried foods

In Ayurvedic medicine, there is a way of categorizing foods, thoughts, experiences, and people. The terms used are in the Sanskrit language from India, and therefore not familiar to most Westerners. They are tamasic, rajasic, and sattvic. Fried foods are heavy and oily and therefore considered tamasic. They cause us to gain weight, to become dull and lethargic, and are most definitely not immune- or hormone-balancing.

When we add salsa or hot sauce to whatever was deep fried, we have just added a food that is considered rajasic. Rajasic foods create heat in the mind and body. If over-indulged in, they can literally burn us right up. So those spicy chicken wings make you a dullard with a hot temper around Super Bowl time!

The Swap

Sattvic foods nourish and strengthen us on all levels, building our prana or life force. We feel fabulous when we ingest them and know we have done something very good for ourselves. These foods are organic, seasonal, obtained close to where they were grown, and high in energy (not processed, genetically modified, or fried). We think clearly, are energized, feel loving, and our skin glows when we eat sattvic foods. Some examples of sattvic foods include most fresh, organic vegetables and fruits, almonds and seeds, ghee, and so on.

4. Non-Organic Foods

Foods that have been coated in pesticides, genetically modified, or grown in soil that has been stripped of nutrients are not going to enhance your vitality or life force. Likewise, eating animals raised in close quarters without sunlight, pumped full of hormones and steroids, and fed low-energy foods full of pesticides will not aid in balancing your immune or hormone systems. Research is now showing that these kinds of toxicants can actually cause your genes to manifest as disease. You can go your whole life and never know you were wired genetically for a disease if you never turn it on. The good news is you can also turn these genes off if you know you have them and then make the right epigenetic or lifestyle choices.

This is what I love about practicing medicine in our day and age. It's exciting to be able to look at my patients' genetics, functional medicine laboratory data, and put the clues together from their stories to really personalize their healthcare plan. This is true preventive medicine.

The Swap

Make sure you seek out grass-fed meats, wild-caught fish, pastured eggs (not just free range), and cruelty-free poultry. These choices will boost your life force because the animal you are eating lived a life of vitality themselves.

Always look for the stickers that start with a "9" on your produce. That "9" means it is organic and not genetically modified. You can go to the Environmental Working Group Website to find alternatives for household cleaners, cosmetics, yard aids, and non-organically grown foods. One of the phrases they coined is the "clean 15" and the "Dirty Dozen" (www.ewg.org). I have listed them here.

The Clean 15	
Avocado	Papayas
Corn	Kiwi
Pineapple	Eggplant
Cabbage	Grapefruit
Frozen sweet peas	Cantaloupe
Onions	Cauliflower
Asparagus	Sweet potatoes
Mangoes	

The Dirty Dozen Plus (always buy organic)	
Apples	Cucumbers
Peaches	Cherry tomatoes
Nectarines	Snap peas
Strawberries	(imported)
Grapes	Potatoes
Celery	Hot peppers
Spinach	Kale and collard
Sweet bell peppers	greens

5. Coffee

Coffee can cause inflammation, depending on your genetics. Some people can metabolize it and others cannot. Regardless of your genetics, however, coffee is acidic. Acidity can cause inflammation and disrupt your immune and hormone balance.

Once again, from the world of Ayurveda, there is a great way of finding out if you can tolerate caffeine without it harming your health in terms of the three constitutional types or doshas.

Vata - Coffee is not good for a vata-dominant person. It is too heating and caffeine can contribute to the spaciness, anxiety, and lack of focus that can be present with a vata imbalance.

Pitta - Coffee is too heating and acidic for a pitta-dominant person. Incidentally, pitta people gravitate to coffee to help them be "more productive." It can be quite damaging to their hormones and energy in the long run, burning them out and causing weight gain.

Kapha - This is the only dosha type that can tolerate coffee. It helps with their metabolism and can aid them in getting off the couch and moving.

The Swap

I recommend you try a product called capomo. It's called the maya nut and grows in Central America. It's alkaline, caffeine free, and does not cause inflammation or disrupt your hormones. It tastes and smells much like coffee and is brewed like coffee. Try it and let me know what you think. I love it. You can create gourmet lattes that will rival those from the most famous of coffee chains. For the recipe see page 149.

6. Gluten

In spite of bread being called the "staff of life" we have a 400% rise in gluten sensitivity every year in the U.S. You likely know if you eat a candy bar and chase it with a soda you are shortening your life. However, did you know a slice of whole wheat bread could be doing the same thing?

Bread contains a protein found in wheat, rye, spelt, barley, and kamut called gluten. People with gluten sensitivity or celiac disease (diagnosed or undiagnosed) have a higher risk of death from inflammatory conditions such as heart disease, autoimmunity, and many cancers.

The most serious form of allergy to gluten is called celiac disease. Celiac disease affects 1 in 100 people, or 3 million Americans, most of whom don't know they have it. But milder forms of gluten sensitivity are even more common and may affect up to one-third of the American population. An estimated 99 percent of people who have a problem with eating gluten don't even know it, yet it's 100% manageable.

There are many autoimmune diseases that can be caused by eating gluten:

- Osteoporosis
- Irritable bowel disease
- Inflammatory bowel disease
- Anemia
- Cancer
- Fatigue
- Canker sores
- Rheumatoid arthritis

- Lupus

- Multiple sclerosis

- All other autoimmune diseases

- Anxiety

- Depression

- Schizophrenia

- Dementia

- Migraines

- Epilepsy

- Neuropathy (nerve damage)

- Autism

It's essential to treat any imbalance at the root cause. Treating gluten sensitivity means treating leaky gut, or intestinal permeability syndrome. Just removing gluten from your diet is not enough.

Please do not buy "gluten-free" processed products from the store. These are no better for you than eating their gluten-filled cousins. In fact, food manufacturers have made a killing by removing wheat from baked goods and adding sugar instead. Gluten-free baked goods found in a store are full of sugar, and therefore just as inflammation promoting.

The Swap

Make your baked goods at home. The easy-to-bake paleo breads, muffins, and cookies found in this book are delicious and will not promote inflammation if eaten in moderation. You can find my master recipe templates on pages 169, 173, and 207.

Try them out and see if you miss gluten. I think they taste better than "normal"

white-flour and white-sugar-filled desserts. Take these options to parties and you will have people asking for your recipes. They won't be able to tell the difference in the taste, but they will notice a big difference in how they feel after the party is over. No food hangover with these goodies.

7. Soy

Aside from wheat and corn, soy is one of the most highly genetically engineered crops in our food supply today.

A team of researchers traveled to Okinawa, Japan in the 1970s to study why the people of Okinawa so often lived past the 100-year mark with such vitality and energy. What they came home with was this: The Japanese people eat soy. What was omitted in the report from these researchers was the fact that Okinawans live in multi-generational communities. The report didn't stress that these centurians eat fresh fish and sea vegetables daily. It seems they didn't notice the fact that these Japanese people eat fresh organic vegetables in every meal. They did not publicize the fact that the people of Okinawa walk daily and eat only what fits in a rice bowl—with chop sticks (implying more slowly than we eat).

Consequently, we got soy added to our food supply. We even began genetically engineering it. We were told that it's good for us and a wonderful protein alternative. What we were not told is that soy is an estrogen disruptor the way it's consumed in the U.S. (in large amounts, heavy with pesticides, GMOs, and powdered to be used as "an enrichment additive").

Soy affects hormone production for both men and women. It is a primary reason for thyroid disorders, hormone imbalances, the pandemic rates of female autoimmune incidence, and some cancers.

When in Japan, have a Japanese-sized serving of fermented, organic tofu. When in America, avoid the soy and gluten-rich "vegetarian meat alternatives" in the freezer section of your local grocery store. Avoid soy-based protein powders, soy milk, and soy sauce.

The Swap

Try coconut aminos as a soy sauce alternative and choose protein in whole food form instead of fake meats.

Coconut milk or homemade nut milks are a great alternative to soy milk. My favorite recipe for nut milk is actually a seed milk. You will find it on page 123.

Seven Mental Hormone and Immune Disruptor Swaps

As you now know, your thoughts and feelings are digested by your mind and heart, much the same way food is digested by your digestive system. What you get from food is nourishment that provides your cells with energy, vitality, and continued life. What you get from nourishing thoughts and feelings are the actions that contribute to your life purpose. If you eat junk food, you will have junk cells and unhealthy tissue development. If you have junk thoughts, you will then engage in junk activity (like watching television, partying, over-working for the wrong reasons, wasting time on your computer, or engaging in other addictive behaviors) that will not motivate the "right action" you need to fulfill a life of purpose and legacy.

Stress slows down your body's ability to digest your food. Stress also slows down your body's ability to digest your emotions, feelings, and experiences. The Adverse Childhood Experiences Study[*] (ACE Study) and the Healing Un-Resolved Trauma (HURT) Study[†] have both proven this fact scientifically. You can read Solving the Autoimmune Puzzle to read more about the HURT and ACEs studies, to take the ACEs Quiz, and to learn how to resolve early trauma and to reverse the effects of an ACE score of one or more.

This book gives you the first step in reducing the inflammation and the inflammatory illnesses that can be a result of chronic stress or a high ACE score. Always start with food, the food you eat and "food for thought." Think of your thoughts, the experiences you have, and your beliefs as food that must be metabolized, the same as what you put on the end of your fork and in your cup.

Again, the ability to change your brain, express your genetics in a healthy way and to detox old hurts takes *willingness*. Willingness is the first and most important quality to engender in yourself as you learn to reverse your autoimmunity and inflammation.

Observe your mental habits and how you react to the same situations in the same way in your life. It takes conscious awareness (and

---

[*]The ACE Study was conducted by the Centers for Disease Control and Prevention (CDC) and Kaiser Permanente between 1995 and 1997. The ACEs Study's results indicate that mistreatment and household dysfunction in the early years contribute to slowed digestion, altered hormones, and immune system changes that then cause death and disability decades later.
[†]The HURT Study was conducted by Dr. Keesha Ewers in 2013 as a small pilot study of 100 women. The HURT Study's results indicate that early trauma that is unresolved in adulthood contributes to low libido in women as well as the chronic illnesses we see in our society today, including autoimmune disease.

most likely trauma healing psychotherapy) to change the patterns you have been repeating throughout your life, just as it takes coaching to change your nutritional habits.

There are many thoughts, beliefs, and feelings that can create hormone and immune havoc, leaving you feeling exhausted and burned out. In fact, this is where we can have the biggest digestive problems—in our minds. I have only listed 7 hormone and immune-disrupting thoughts and beliefs, but spend some time thinking of others that might be trapping you in your life.

1. Shame

Shame is an emotion that is a sure inflammation enhancer. You are not capable of feeling love and shame at the same time. Shame creates contraction in your body; whereas love is experienced as openness. Autoimmunity is a hypervigilant immune system. A hypervigilant mind creates a hypervigilant immune system.

The Swap

If you are feeling shame, find a moment in your life that you have felt love and spend time with that thought instead of the one causing you pain.

2. Hate

Hate usually arises because someone has betrayed or hurt you deeply. Hate is not an emotion that can coincide with vibrant health. The way out of hate is forgiveness. You have likely heard this before and are rolling your eyes right now. But let me just stop you before you quit reading here. I am not saying you have to reconcile with anyone who has caused you harm. I believe in having healthy boundaries with toxic people. Forgiveness and reconciliation are not the same thing. I discuss this in more detail in *Solving the Autoimmune Puzzle.*

The Swap

Think of the personality trait the person who hurt you exhibited that you really hate. Is it selfishness? Is it cruelty? Is it misusing power? How about a lack of integrity? Write any and all of the ego characteristics you find in the person you are focusing on right now in your journal.

Next find this person in your heart as if you are looking in the mirror. They are only reflecting the very human personality traits that you, me, and everyone else on this planet have. We all have the same traits! It's true. We just act on them differently so it looks like we are so very different from the one we hate.

For example, Adolf Hitler could be said to have misused power and acted cruelly. I can say that I have done both of those things (maybe even before breakfast today because I'm a mom and have to really watch not using the old guilt treatment on my teenagers). I have never bought tanks and taken over Poland. I have never killed anyone. I will never do those things . . . BUT I have manifested two of the personality traits I can identify in Hitler.

Make sense? Try it yourself. Go deep and don't be afraid to really look at what triggers you. You do it too, just differently than the one you hate.

This leads to forgiveness. When you are no longer blaming, judging, hating the other person, you can more readily forgive.

Remember what Mark Twain said so eloquently, "Not forgiving is like you drinking poison and expecting the other guy to die." Or the Chinese proverb that says, "Don't forgive, dig two graves instead of one." You can think of hatred as a toxic additive to your diet.

3. I have to be perfect to be loved

This one is a mental cage that you will never flourish in. You are worthy of love just by grace. By virtue of being who you are—a gift to this world with your own unique talents and skills you bring. You are lovable just as you are.

I cannot tell you how many people I have worked with in therapy that are trapped by the perfection myth. Every single patient who comes to see me who has an autoimmune disease is a perfectionist. It's part of what I call the *autoimmune mindset*. It's something you decided when you were a small child in response to events you didn't know how to process differently.

The Swap

Go pick up that little girl or boy inside you and let him or her know just how much YOU love her. Let her know she doesn't have to DO anything for you to love her. She just has to be herself and you will support and adore her no matter what. Forgive yourself for thinking anything else. Forgive your body for its weaknesses. Forgive yourself when you indulge in foods that cause inflammation and create hormone havoc in your body. If you can forgive yourself without shame, you will willingly get right back to your healthy food plan. You will not feel full vitality until you can do this. Take it from me. I know. This was my story until I re-wrote it and set myself free.

4. I am not safe

How can you possibly feel free if you do not feel safe? If you are truly not safe, then make the necessary changes to make yourself safe. Every woman, man, and child deserve to live free from harm. Unfortunately, many in our world do not. If you are reading this, you are likely in a position to create safety in your life if you set your mind and considerable will to it.

Not feeling safe is a result of a childhood trauma, stressor, or experience you did not have the skills to process. You likely had good reason to feel unsafe. Ask yourself now if it's still true that you are not safe.

What triggers anxiety in you today? Is it a big red button that you are hypervigilant about? Is it pressed all too easily? If so, it is a good idea to get some work with a trained EMDR therapist or a therapist who is certified in Brainspotting or clinical hypnotherapy.

A zebra being chased by a lion is not going to feel safe. The zebra knows it's not safe to stop and go to the bathroom or to have a baby when it's in danger. Are you a zebra? Is your libido gone? Do you have bowel issues? Are your hormones imbalanced? Is your immune system attacking you?

Feeling unsafe plays havoc on your hormone and immune systems and can lead to obesity, fatigue, sleeplessness, low sexual desire, PMS, hot flashes, vaginal dryness, memory issues, brain fog, autoimmunity, and more.

The Swap

The next time you are triggered by someone who leaves you feeling abandoned, unsafe, lonely, or hurt, close your eyes. Take a deep breath and really feel where those unsafe emotions are in your body.

In your shoulders? In your gut? In your throat, jaw, or chest?

Now ask yourself how old you feel.

Are you very, very young?

Go get that little one and give her a big hug and reassure her that whatever she experienced as a child is not going to happen again because you are watching over her and keeping her safe.

Bring her into your heart and love her. Feel how safe you both are.

Breathe that feeling of grounded safety into the area of tension in your body.

Do this until you are relaxed again.

5. I don't have enough

Scarcity complex is an insidious trap that haunts you if you have thoughts of "not enough time," "not enough friends," "not enough energy," "not enough money," "not enough connection with my partner," "not enough. . . ." Whenever you are having these thoughts, you are triggering your fight-or-flight nervous system, becoming the chased zebra again. You now know this leads to disrupted digestion on all levels. It won't matter how healthy your food choices are if you are eating your meals with a hypervigilant nervous system.

The Swap

Write a positive affirmation that affirms your abundance. Whatever we spend time thinking about comes true, so make sure your thoughts are something you want to manifest.

For example:

- "I easily and effortlessly attract abundance of all kinds into my life. I am grateful for all of the love, resources, time, and energy I possess."

- "I love and appreciate my body and feel gratitude for it just as it is."

- "Not only am I enough, but I am perfect just as I am, with my own unique talents and gifts I offer to this world."

- "I easily and effortlessly provide my body with the wholesome nutrients it needs to engage in my life purpose."

6. I will be happy when . . .

This is a black hole that leads straight to inflammation if there ever was one.

Have you ever caught yourself thinking, "I will be happy when I lose weight," or "I will be happy when I have a boyfriend or a partner or get married," "I will be happy when I can finally pay off my bills," "or get that promotion," and so on . . .

The Swap

Find all of the things in your life you can be grateful for. Gratitude is powerful medicine and puts you on the road to healing quickly. Keeping a gratitude journal is a wonderful daily practice. We all have something to feel grateful for, but we often lose sight of those things because our challenges seem to fill the viewing screens of our minds.

When you wake up in the morning, begin with expressing gratitude for the very fact that you woke up. Then start listing even the very smallest things you can think of. They all add up to an infinite number of blessings to be grateful for.

- Did you wake up in a bed with a roof over your head?

- Are you getting out of bed and stepping on two feet that can still carry you around?

- Are you about to brush teeth that you are lucky enough to be able to chew your food with?

- Can you see with your eyes to know where to go?

- Do you have food to eat, clean water to drink?

So many blessings and so little time to express thanks for them. When you fill your mind with thoughts of appreciation, it fosters love—and love is the best medicine of all.

7. I can't

I consider sugar one of the biggest toxins there is. Yet sugar is not your biggest enemy. Self-limiting beliefs trump sugar in terms of inflammation and toxicity by far.

Self-limiting beliefs keep you caged. You are not free to live to your highest potential. The worst part of this is you are doing it to yourself. If you ever hear yourself think or say, "I can't _____ (fill in the blank)" then STOP.

Realize you just put yourself in a cage of your own making.

The Swap

I challenge you to say "I can" whenever you get the chance. Does this mean you say yes to everyone who wants you to volunteer for their organization? Does it mean you over schedule yourself so your own self-care goes out the window? No. You get to tell people no. You get to set healthy boundaries for yourself.

What it does mean is this: You say "I can" when you are wanting to do something new that can stretch you a little bit more. It means you go beyond your own self-imposed limits.

Make this the week of "I can." Then make it a month of "I can." Then try a year of "I can." By then you will be on your way to a lifetime of accepting the opportunities that come your way that Life is putting in your path for your growth and maximization of your potential. If I can do this, so can you . . .

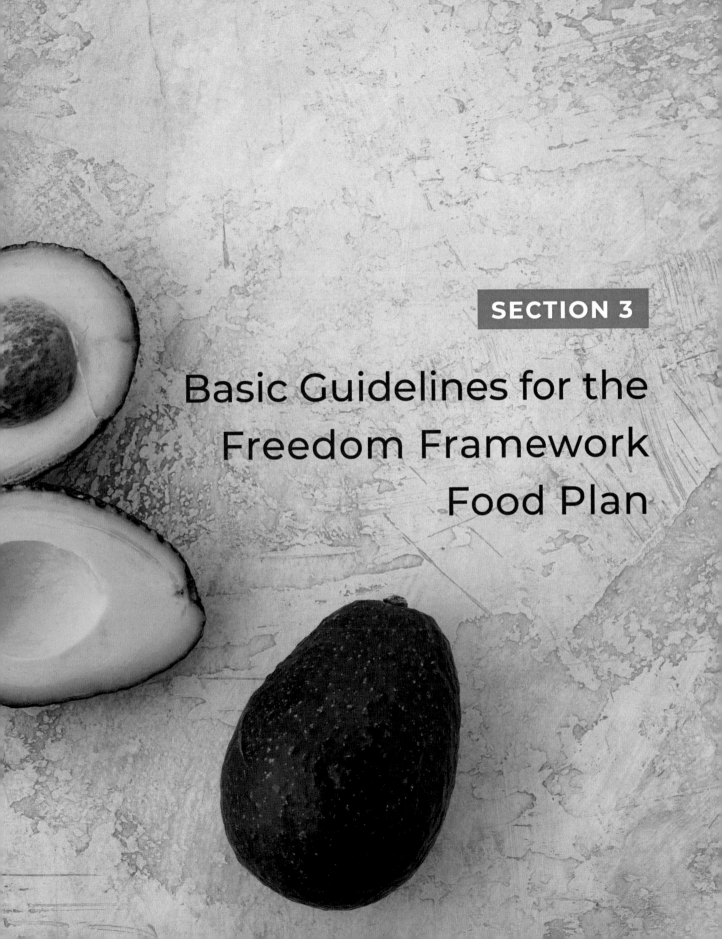

Basic Guidelines for the Freedom Framework Food Plan

The Freedom Framework Food Plan

The Plan

The Basic Guidelines for the Freedom Framework Food Plan

1. Eat 10-12 cups of fresh, organic, seasonal vegetables in a rainbow of colors.
2. Decrease or eliminate grains and replace with plant sources of carbohydrates.
3. Replace unhealthy fats with healthy ones.
4. Only eat humanely raised meats and eggs.
5. Eliminate sugar, gluten, dairy, soy, GMO substances, stimulants, and chemicals.
6. Eat for your body type (Ayurvedic and genetic).
7. If you need to lose weight, eat only in an 8-hour period.
8. Use food as medicine as determined by laboratory testing and dosha balance.
9. Eat in a stress-free environment.
10. Make sure your relationship with your food and your body is a healthy one.

The Freedom Framework Food Plan can be described as an anti-inflammatory, low-glycemic index, gluten-free, grain-free, dairy free, soy free, complex carbohydrate, high quality fat, whole foods way of eating and nourishing your body. The plan focuses on supporting cellular health through the use of therapeutic and medicinal foods that improve immune function, hormone balance, and energy production through the support of your mitochondria.

Mitochondria are the little engines in every cell that make energy by transforming the nutrients and oxygen from your food into life force for you. Unhealthy food choices can lead to mitochondrial death, and subsequently premature aging of your brain, heart, nervous system, immune system, and organs. Healthy mitochondria make for a reduction of risk for neurological diseases, autoimmunity, and cancer. The Freedom Framework Food Plan's focus is to teach you to eat the right quantity and quality of fats, proteins, and carbohydrates so you can burn fat, grow muscle, and maintain a healthy hormone balance and immune system function.

Why Follow the Freedom Framework Food Plan?

Cellular and mitochondrial damage are accelerated with the standard American diet (SAD). The typical packaged foods that are loaded with chemical preservatives, food dyes, sugar, sugar substitutes, genetically modified substances, gluten, and followed up with cruel animal practices. These cause inflammation, degenerative neurological diseases such as Parkinson's disease, Alzheimer's disease, multiple sclerosis (MS), amyotrophic lateral sclerosis (ALS) and other autoimmune diseases like diabetes, rheumatoid arthritis, lupus, Raynaud's syndrome, psoriasis, eczema, rosacea, Hashimoto's thyroiditis, Grave's disease, osteoporosis, Crohn's disease, ulcerative colitis, and many more.

This food plan was developed over a period of 30 years of medical practice and countless hours of education and certifications in functional medicine, nutrition, and Ayurvedic medicine. This is the plan I teach at the Academy for Integrative Medicine to my integrative medicine health coach students. This is the plan I give to my patients. This plan is the one I used to reverse my own autoimmune disease and breast cancer without medications or surgery. This plan works. It's easy to follow and requires minimal time in the kitchen. All you need is willingness. Willingness to care for and nourish yourself. Willingness to try something new. Willingness to give up the need for an expected outcome. Willingness to understand that all of it, including disease, is being done for you and not to you. Willingness to see the perfection in the imperfection.

Recommendations

Eat 10-12 Cups of Fresh Organic Seasonal Vegetables in a Rainbow of Colors

Your cells need oxygen to thrive. However, oxygen in the wrong amounts and in the wrong places can cause "rust" in the cells, or what is known as oxidative damage from free radicals. This oxidative damage can be mitigated by eating vegetables, spices and herbs that have anti-oxidant properties such as glutathione, vitamin C and vitamin E. The more colorful your plate is, the more phytonutrients you will be consuming, and this will result in healthier cells and more graceful aging.

The anti-inflammatory effects of phytonutrients are well documented in science. The more variety of color, the more phytonutrient dense your diet is, the more anti-inflammatory affects you will experience. You can think of this food plan as a wonderful replacement for non-steroidal anti-inflammatory drugs such as ibuprofen and Advil.

Eating plenty of fresh vegetables provides your body with carbohydrates. The word carbohydrate is often considered a dirty word these days. However, they are necessary, in combination with clean protein and healthy fat choices, to fuel your body and brain with energy. There are two kinds of carbohydrates: simple and complex. Simple carbs are those that are rapidly converted to glucose by your body. They quickly spike your blood sugar when you eat them, which can result in a drop in energy, mood, and focus. If you eat too many of them, they will be stored by your body as fat. Examples of simple carbohydrates are bread, sugary drinks, white rice, pastries, and pasta.

Complex carbs are more slowly digested and take longer to make an impact on your blood sugar, therefore making them easier for your endocrine system to handle. Fruits and vegetables are complex carbohydrates and a great source of fiber too.

I am often asked where fiber will come from if grains are eliminated. This is a great question. The answer is in the 10-12 cups of vegetables you eat in a day. Fiber is extremely important for a healthy digestive system and daily bowel movements. Eliminating your toxins in the form of 1-3 banana shaped brown bowel movements a day is vital for your health. If you don't take out the trash in your kitchen, it will build up, spill out of your trash can, and eventually attract vermin to your kitchen. This is exactly what can happen in your body if you don't take out your body's trash at least daily. The vermin you attract to your digestive system comes in the form of yeast, bacterial overgrowth, and parasites. It's important for you to get at least 30 grams of fiber a day. Most of that should come from vegetables.

There are two kinds of fiber; insoluble and soluble. Insoluble fiber adds bulk and helps you move the solid waste from your body. This kind of fiber doesn't dissolve in water. Examples of insoluble fiber are celery, the skin from root vegetables, cabbage, dark leafy greens, zucchini, and broccoli.

Soluble fiber helps absorb toxins from the gut, helps to lower cholesterol, helps to keep your blood sugar balanced and gives you a feeling of satiety, or fullness. Soluble fiber absorbs water and slows your digestion down. Examples of soluble fiber are carrots, chia and flax seeds, berries, apples, and nuts.

You will get plenty of fiber if you pay attention and consume all of your daily veggies. This is also where your "brain food" and energy will come from when you leave sugar, stimulants like coffee, and grains behind. Sometimes when people start out with this food plan, they feel tired and weak and experience brain fog. What I usually find is a little extra squash, an increase in

healthy fats, and/or some additional protein will take care of it within a day. Do not eliminate grains without replacing them with a rainbow of vegetables.

Decrease or Eliminate Grains and Replace with Plant Sources of Carbohydrates

The modern industrialized way of milling grain is fast and efficient. It allows what we now call flour to be shipped so we can "feed the world." It lasts seemingly forever and is pretty much pest resistant, because it's devoid of nutritional value. Wheat was the first modern milled grain. It created stability for wide distribution and a prolonged shelf life. However, this modern "miracle" has created a nutritional mess worldwide.

According to the Weston A. Price Foundation, the modern milling process robbed the original wheat strains of:

Thiamine (B1) 77%	Potassium 77%
Riboflavin (B2) 80%	Sodium 78%
Niacin 81%	Chromium 40%
Pyridoxine (B6) 72%	Manganese 86%
Pantothenic acid 50%	Iron 76%
	Cobalt 89%
Vitamin E 86%	Zinc 78%
Calcium 60%	Copper 68%
Phosphorous 71%	Selenium 16%
Magnesium 84%	Molybdenum 48%

As if this isn't bad enough, now we have genetically altered our wheat supply in such a way that our bodies cannot recognize it as food. Your immune system is designed to attack anything that it cannot recognize as "you." Although wheat is the largest crop in our country, is now drought resistant, pest resistant, and easier to grow than ever before, it's also full of gluten that many humans and other animals can no longer tolerate. Not only does it cause inflammatory issues, such as autoimmune disease, but also obesity, dementia, and cancer.

So should you replace your wheat pasta, bread, and pastries with gluten-free versions? Unfortunately, it's not that simple. Chronic inflammation is the root of all disease and can be caused by or exacerbated by the processed "flours" and sugar that are used in most gluten-free baked products. This cookbook gives you master recipe templates for popular baked goods that replaces flour with some easier-to-digest ingredients, such as almond meal, hazelnut meal, and coconut flour. These replacements are not used in the same ratios that you would use white flour, so you will be disappointed with your results if you try to just replace them cup for cup in your favorite recipe. Use the recipes provided in this book and practice a new way of making your favorite baked goods.

Knowing that there are different "weights" to flours also helps when you are learning a new way of baking. Replacing one weight of flour with the same weight will help you keep your cooking chemistry balanced. Here are some examples of flour weights.

Heavy-Weight Flours
Almond - Almond flour is ground finer than almond meal is, but both can be used for baking. Almond flour makes a nicer consistency for the cake recipe in this book. Almond flour has a higher oil content and is higher in protein than wheat flour. It can go rancid, so store it in an air-tight container in the freezer when you're not using it.
Chestnut - Chestnut flour has a nutty taste and can be used in lieu of almond flour if you have a sensitivity to almonds.
Coconut - Coconut flour is high in fiber and absorbs liquids in a recipe quickly. Small amounts go a long way. It has a strong coconut flavor and is best used when baking sweeter recipes.
Garbanzo bean - Garbanzo bean flour is great for pizza crust when you don't want to use cauliflower. It's high in protein and fiber and can easily be used to make Indian flat breads or tortillas.

Medium-Weight Flours
Buckwheat - Great for pancakes, although I like mine without any flour.
Oat - Make sure it's gluten free. Oat flour is higher in carbohydrates than nut and seed flours, so I never use it.
Millet - Has a nutty taste and can be used to make Indian flat breads like chapati.

Light-Weight Flours
Arrowroot - My daughters love to use arrowroot to create a fluffier texture in their baked goods. I find I don't tolerate it and actually prefer a chewier texture in my cookies. You can also use arrowroot as a thickening agent for sauces.
Tapioca Flour – It can be used in the same way arrowroot is used. I also find that a sprinkling is useful for rolling out pie crust.
Potato Starch - Potato starch can be used interchangeably with arrowroot or tapioca flour.

When you soak and sprout nuts and seeds and then grind them for cooking, they are even easier to digest than the nut meal you can purchase commercially. When nuts or seeds are soaked and sprouted, their acidity is reduced and enzymes are released that help facilitate digestion and absorption.

You can only sprout raw nuts and seeds. Cover your raw seeds or nuts with 2 inches of filtered water and leave them on the countertop overnight. The next morning drain and rinse them.

To sprout your seeds or nuts, spread the soaked nuts or seeds on a baking sheet and cover with a cheesecloth. Rinse them twice daily. Once you see a little white sprout coming from the narrow end of the nut or seed, you can store them in the refrigerator for 2-3 days or use them that day.

You can use soaked and sprouted seeds or nuts as granola, grind them to make flour, blend them with water to make nut or seed milk, or use them as a topping on your chia-seed pudding or breakfast cereal or salads.

Gluten is a protein found in many grains such as wheat, spelt, rye, and barley. Modern grains and gluten are a primary source of inflammation and the pandemic rise of autoimmune disease. Inflammatory chemicals that are released by the body's response to gluten break down the protective barrier of the gut wall, the arteries and veins of the circulatory system, and causes inflammation in the brain, resulting in memory and cognitive decline. Some people can tolerate what are known as pseudo-grains and grasses. These plants are lower on the glycemic index scale than grains such as wheat, corn, rye, barley, oats, rice, and sorghum. They are also higher in protein. They include quinoa, buckwheat, teff, millet, amaranth, and wild rice.

The recipe templates in this cookbook offer you a simple way to eliminate gluten and gluten-containing grains from your life for good. Stocking your pantry with the necessary food swaps ahead of time will eliminate any chance for you to falter in your energy-boosting and life force-building plan. Remember that the energy you need to fulfill your life's purpose is contained in what you put on the end of your fork, in your cup, and in your mind. Be mindful in all ways.

Replace Unhealthy Fats with Healthy Ones

Your brain is 60% fat. Fats are essential for proper hormone balance, nervous system function and brain health. If you have inflammatory skin issues, it's likely part of the solution lies in changing your ratio of healthy fats. If your eyesight is compromised, once again the answer is likely partly healthy fats in the right ratios and proportions. Low fat is not healthy. The low-fat revolution caused a national pandemic of diabesity. Eating healthy fats will not make you skinny, contrary to what some popular book titles promise. As with everything, it depends on your body type and genetics.

Your body is made from cells swimming in salt water—basically the same ratio of salt to water as the ocean. Your brain is mostly fat and the peptides gleaned from protein and runs primarily on specialized sugars. Contrary to what we thought in the

1970's, fat is not bad for you. However, fried food, trans fats, hydrogenated oils, and an unhealthy ratio of fats will not create the essential fats required for the creation and maintenance of healthy cell membranes, hormones, and the nervous system.

Fats absorb toxins, which then get into the cells. When this happens, the body needs a replacement of good healthy fats, especially if you are going to absorb the fat-soluble vitamins A, E, and D3. The proper maintenance of the fatty cell membrane is essential for the exchange of electrolytes necessary to fire the electrical impulses that power your muscles, such as your heart and even your circadian rhythm. You are an electrical being, which is why daily "grounding" with healthy fats is so essential.

Use this acronym to remember the right kinds of fat to focus on: BACON

B: Butter and ghee
A: Avocado
C: Coconut oil, coconut cream, and coconut milk
O: Olive oil
N: Nuts and seeds

Other healthy fats come from fish, which contains omega 3 docosahexaenoic acid (DHA) and eicosapenthaenoic acid (EPA). Wild-caught sources of smaller fish are the best as they will contain fewer environmental pollutants. Plant sources are flax, hemp, chia, and marine algae. Make sure your fish oil is from a high-quality source. You will get what you pay for. Never purchase fish oil from a drug store, big box store, online from discount retailers, or from a vitamin shop or grocery store. The brands sold by functional medicine providers have been vetted and tested by third-party sources to ensure their quality.

When you buy oil, make sure it's organic, cold pressed, and unrefined. Since fats and oils are easily damaged by contact with air, heat, light, and plastic, it's important to know how to buy and store your oils. It's also essential not to overheat certain kinds of oils as they can become toxic and cause inflammation. Here's a simple guide for understanding, buying, cooking, and storing oils and fats.

Buying and Storing Fats and Oils	
Do	**Don't**
Buy oils bottled in dark glass.	Buy oils in plastic containers.
Store your fats protected from light away from heat sources.	Store your oils in the open light next to the stove or a pilot light.
Keep your oils tightly sealed.	Keep your fats loosely sealed.

Oil Definitions

Refined Oil	Heat or chemically extracted oils are known as refined. This process leaves the oil more heat stable, but can also damage some of the nutritional profile of the oil.
Unrefined Oil	Cold-pressed oils that are not heated or chemically treated. They are more likely to have their vitamins, enzymes, and nutrients left intact. Cold-pressed coconut oil, and virgin and extra-virgin olive oils are examples of unrefined oils.
Virgin Oil	Virgin oils come from the second pressing of the oil source. They are not as heat resistant and ought to be used in salad dressings or on top of food rather than heated.
Extra Virgin Oil	Extra-virgin oils are cold pressed and un-refined and are from the first pressing of the oil source. They meet a more rigid set of standards for quality than those that are labeled virgin.
Cold-pressed Oil	Cold pressed oils are "pressed" from the oil source without the use of heat or chemicals, and therefore nutrients are better preserved in the final product.
Pure Oil	Pure oils are a blend of first-pressed refined and un-refined oils and therefore are likely to have been subjected to heat and/or chemicals.

How to Choose the Right Oil for Your Recipe

High heat oils: can be used for frying at 400°F

Avocado oil
Coconut oil
Grapeseed oil
Peanut oil
Sesame oil

Medium heat oils: can be used for sautéing at 350°F

Almond oil
Butter or ghee
Olive oil
Walnut oil

Low heat oils: can be used for anything under 350°F

Hemp oil
Fish oil
Flax oil
Olive oil
Sesame oil
Any nut oil

Only Eat Humanely Raised Meats and Eggs

It is now a well-known fact that current agricultural practices are not only cruel but use chemicals that are hormone disruptors and toxic to the animal as well as humans. Grain-fed animals are fed antibiotics, pesticides, hormones, and herbicides. All of these toxins are then ingested by you when you eat them, which places a burden on your detoxification system and slows your metabolism.

There is a difference between mainstream agricultural practices and what is known as biodynamic ones. Most people have heard the term "organic" at this point. Organic certification is a national standard given by certifying bodies to ensure there have been no artificial chemicals used to grow crops or animals or the feed that is fed to the animals.

Biodynamic is farming at an even higher level of attention to chemical-free food than the label organic provides. Biodynamic farming is growing food the way nature intended. Biodynamic farmers use biological mixtures to enliven the soil and use no artificial chemicals. Special attention is given to how crops are rotated and animals are pastured and fed. Biodynamics was first developed in the early 1920's by Dr. Rudolf Steiner, the founder of anthroposophy. Anthroposophy is a philosophical system established by Dr. Steiner that seeks to use natural ways to optimize physical and mental health and well-being. Biodynamic farming practices are meant to contribute to our physical and mental health and well-being, not just feed us calories.

Biodynamic farming focuses on soil health as the foundation to sustainable farming and looks at soil as a living organism. This focus yields more nutrient-dense crops, which means better feed for animals and healthier food for humans. Working the land in this way puts the farmer in harmony with the cycles and rhythms of nature, rather than at odds with it. There is no need for genetic modification, chemicals and pesticides, hormones, and antibiotics when food is grown in microbial diverse and dense soil that is in relationship with and reflective of the planet we live on. In fact, you could say that the focus on the microbiome of the gut for optimal health is also biodynamic farming, in the human digestive system. We are but microcosms of the macrocosm of the universe we live in.

Grass-fed and free-range animals that are raised humanely and slaughtered as humanely as possible will pass a different kind of life force to the person who eats them. Not only that, but the ratio of fatty acids is far different from those of grain-fed animals. The same is true for eggs that come from grain-fed chickens as opposed to biodynamically pastured chickens (not free-range or cage-free).

Avoid farm-raised and Atlantic fish for the same reasons. Choose instead cold-water fish such as sardines (smaller fish are less likely to carry a toxic load), salmon, and mackerel. Wild game such as pheasant, venison, and elk are also great choices. Make sure you use as much of the animal as possible. You can start by making bone broth from the bones. Eating animals and plants raised with this sort of consciousness promotes a biodynamically diverse range of microbes in your own body.

Eliminate Sugar, Gluten, Dairy, Soy, GMO Substances, Stimulants, and Chemicals

Breaking the sugar habit was probably the hardest part of my own autoimmune reversal. This had to include solving the puzzle of why I craved sweets. Your relationship with food is just as important as what you actually eat because this relationship informs how and what you eat.

So why can't people break the sweet habit for good?

For Emergency "Beast Cravings"

If you cannot overcome a craving for a sabotaging food, please begin taking Inositol and NT Balance immediately. You can order both on the DrKeesha. com store. Follow the label instructions for assistance with balancing your blood sugar and neurotransmitters.

If you cannot give up sugar on your own, you may have food allergies, be insulin resistant, have a gut microbial imbalance, or thyroid or other hormone problems that require the assistance of a trained integrative medicine expert in order for you to move forward with your health program.

My team, or one of my Academy for Integrative Medicine trained health coaches, can set up a phone consultation for you where you will get an individualized plan if you are unable to follow the instructions in this program on your own. We are passionate about you learning how to empower you to heal yourself and do this on your own and will provide you with as much information as you need to succeed.

Nondairy "milks" are a delicious alternative to the dairy products that come from our toxic, inhumanely factory-raised animals. You can use seed and nut milks for baking, cooking, on top of the yummy cereal and granola in this book, or drink it along with the low glycemic brownies or cookies you will learn to make from the master recipes in the dessert section. The recipe for how to make seed and nut milks is on page 123.

Fruit-infused waters, seltzers, and teas are a beautiful and tasty alternative to alcoholic drinks or stimulants such as coffee. I also love dandelion tea and capomo as a substitute for coffee. If you are a vata dosha type, you can add your ghee to capomo, just as you would coffee and have far less insomnia, brain fog, jitteriness, and anxiety. Tea-free chai blends are great for all of the dosha types and help to fuel a healthy digestive fire. Play with the tastes and find what suits your desires. Take this on as an adventure, and it won't feel like an overwhelming chore.

Eat for Your Body Type and Listen to the Feedback from Your Body and Mind

I use Ayurveda as a framework for exploring the ways your mind and body provide feedback for how they are doing. According to Ayurveda, we are impacted by everything: our age, the climate, our dosha balance, what we eat, what we think, our experiences; the images we put into our mind through books, movies, the computer and the television; our patterns of sleep, sex, and exercise; and our relationships to everyone and everything we encounter on a minute-to-minute basis. This means your body, mind, and heart are constantly in action, unless you intentionally provide space for them to relax and regenerate. When we live a sattvic, balanced lifestyle in the Ayurvedic way, we will be meditating, doing yoga or exercise for our individual body type, eating according to the needs of our own constitutions, and viewing the world through a positive perceptual filter.

Balancing Vata with Food

If you are a vata-predominate person, are vata imbalanced, live in a vata-aggravating climate, or are in the vata stage of life (after meno or andropause), then grounding is the name of the game. Be guided by the understanding that vata imbalances are made worse by eating beans, raw and cold foods, not following a daily routine, being out in the cold, wet, and wind, and skipping meals.

Vata needs a warm, oily, hydrating, wet, and grounding diet. Soups, stews, warm drinks, curries, raw and sprouted nuts and seeds, healthy fats, warming spices, and cooked whole foods are the best choices for vata people. Avoid lots of gas-producing, raw, cruciferous vegetables like cauliflower, broccoli, Brussels sprouts, cabbage, and unsoaked and sprouted beans. Vata tends to struggle with keeping a strong digestive fire, so it's best to eat small amounts frequently through the day.

Balancing Pitta with Food

People with a pitta-predominate dosha type are used to having cast iron stomachs and the ability to digest just about anything. However, if you are a pitta dosha type, you are likely quite driven and possibly even perfectionistic. This could mean you have spent some of your life trying unsuccessfully to digest pent up frustration, anger, and resentment, which can leave your liver a bit fragile in its ability to

detox your food and emotions. This can lead to inflammatory issues. As a young pitta dosha type, you will likely have experienced being "hangry" if you were not fed on time.

Pitta needs re-mineralizing sea vegetables, raw seeds, coconut oil, sprouted mung beans, avocado, some raw vegetables and vegetable juices (especially in hot climates), and some cooked veggies. They also benefit from fruit-infused waters, smoothies, soaked buckwheat groats, soaked lentils, and cooling spices like mint, basil, and saffron, tulsi, turmeric, and cilantro. Pitta can use coconut sugar and berries sparingly.

Balancing Kapha with Food

Kapha people do well with low-fat, low-carbohydrate, high-fiber, light, warming foods. Kapha is increased with the sweet taste, and kapha people tend to crave sweet foods and sweet experiences. They themselves are usually very sweet. If you are a kapha-predominate dosha type, you might have a hard time keeping your body weight balanced, so it's important to know how to choose the correct portion size for your body type. In Ayurveda, the serving size is known as an Anjali. The correct amount of food for your body type is determined by putting your hands, palms facing up, together to form a bowl. The amount of food that will fit in your bowl is the correct amount of food for you to eat in each meal.

If you are kapha, it's doubly important for you to stop eating by 5:00 pm in the evening. Eat only when you are hungry and drink fresh ginger tea or bone broth with your meals. You can eat 40% raw vegetables and vegetable juices in a day and 60% cooked foods. I am a pitta-kapha person and find that starting my day with freshly juiced vegetables and fresh ginger and cilantro, into which I add 2 tablespoons ground flax seeds for fiber and 20 grams of collagen for protein starts my day with vibrant energy and a balanced blood sugar that doesn't crash later in the morning. I have used this as my breakfast for years and find my skin glows, my brain is clear, my digestive system works, my body is pain free, my hormones are balanced, and my weight remains stable.

Kapha should avoid sweet fruits, heavy fats like avocados, desserts, grains, iced drinks, baked goods, most nuts, and dairy products. Instead, focus on eating lots of green leafy and cruciferous vegetables, fruits like lemons, limes, and pomegranates, quinoa and sprouted buckwheat groats, sprouted mung beans and lentils, and clean protein.

All of the doshas, but especially pitta and kapha, ought to do a liver cleanse four times a year—with each season change. The cleanse needs to be personalized as there is no one-size-fits-all way of detoxing, just as there is no one-size-fits-all way of eating.

Eat Only in an 8-Hour Period If You Need to Lose Weight

I often tell my patients that their digestive system can only handle the amount of food that fits in their cupped hands at each feeding. Ayurveda recommends we leave 1/3 of the stomach empty, so there is room for the digestive process to take place. Picture filling a bowl completely with the ingredients needed to make a cake. If the bowl is filled to the top with almond and coconut flour and eggs, you won't be able to stir the ingredients together without making a mess.

Another analogy I often give is for you to imagine your work or home environment. If you are focused on a task, and you continually get interrupted by kids, the phone, co-workers, or other distractions, you will not be able to do a good job completing your task. The digestive system is the same. If you eat breakfast, and then two hours later ingest more food before your body has had a chance to properly digest your last feeding, your digestive system will become inefficient and unable to do the task of proper digestion, assimilation, and elimination. This will result in a buildup of toxicity in your body, which then leads to skin and joint inflammation, fatigue, brain fog, hormone imbalances, mood disorders, weight gain or loss, microbial imbalance and digestive issues, and eventually autoimmunity and cancer.

Use the Hunger Gauge to determine when you need to eat. If you need to lose weight, I advise eating only during an 8-hour period. This will change your dietary habits by bringing awareness to what is entering your body and the physical sensations that accompany your food intake. Keep a food diary and record your hunger gauge number in your diary each time you eat. The reason for using this tool is simple: Eat when you are hungry and stop when your stomach is full!

Note: You will not eat after 5 pm even though you may be hungry. You are training yourself to eat in a more natural rhythm that matches our human biology and gives your digestive and lymphatic systems a much needed chance to eliminate toxins during the night.

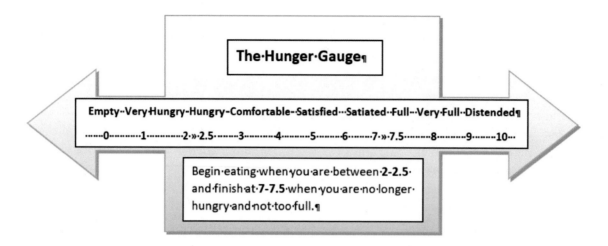

The·Hunger·Gauge

Empty··Very·Hungry-Hungry-Comfortable-Satisfied···Satiated···Full··Very·Full··Distended

······0········1·········2·»·2.5·······3········4·········5········6·······7·»·7.5·······8········9······10···

Begin·eating·when·you·are·between·2-2.5·
and·finish·at·7-7.5·when·you·are·no·longer·
hungry·and·not·too·full.

Use Food as Medicine as Determined by Laboratory Testing and Dosha Balance

According the Naveen Jain, the creator of the microbiome mapping test known as Viome, the super foods that are super for you are determined by the balance of the bugs in your gut. In other words, blueberries might not be a super food for you. Conversely, higher complex carbohydrates and lower protein might be what your gut is asking for. Jain has found that 30% of people who have taken the Viome test have been intolerant of spinach and other oxalate-containing foods (more on this on page __). He has also discovered that some people have their gut wall broken down with low-carb and high-protein diets, leading to an increase in inflammation. Once again, what is medicinal for one might not be medicinal for another.

How can you tell what your personal super foods are? Test, don't guess. In my practice, anyone with autoimmune disease does microbiome stool testing, genetic and organics acid testing, food sensitivity testing, and adrenal and hormone testing.

These are all functional medicine tests that help me put the clues together for my patients who are interested in getting to the root cause of their weight, hormone, digestive, energy, mood, and immune system problems.

When I combine this lab data with the details of my patients' story and their Ayurvedic dosha balance, I am able to give them precise and personalized nutritional plans. Your body will change once you make changes in your lifestyle choices. When that happens, you need to test again and make adjustments that reflect new data. Knowledge is power and the key to reversing disease.

There is a hard-and-fast-rule I use when working with patients and their laboratory results and genetic information: *never treat the gene or the lab test.* This is true for any piece of isolated laboratory data you receive. You are a unique milieu of moving parts, all trying to maintain balance in an environment ever in flux. It's important you do not take one piece of information and run with it, believing it's the smoking gun for all of your health issues.

Your lifestyle choices impact how your microbiome, and therefore your genes, express themselves. The gift of functional medicine testing allows clinicians like me to be precise in creating individualized lifestyle plans which, when combined with other elements of your story and laboratory data, give you a chance to reverse disease, or at the very least halt further progression.

There is no one diet that fits everyone. There is no one exercise plan, supplementation regimen, detoxification program, style of psychotherapy, or "super food" that works the same in every person. This is because we differ genetically, are exposed to different toxins, have our own unique ability to detoxify those toxins, and are digestively different from one another. Again, this is what Ayurvedic medicine taught us many thousands of years ago. Modern science is slowly catching on and catching up.

Eat in a Stress-Free Environment

Most of my patients report feeling overwhelmed in some way when they come to see me—with fatigue, weight issues, gut problems, pain, hormone imbalances, memory loss, and inflammation. This sense of overwhelm negatively affects digestion.

In Chapter Two, we discussed stress and how the fight-or-flight nervous system response shuts down the digestive system.

This can serve a purpose at times, to spur to action and to motivate, but those times are not for eating. As much as possible, eat in a stress-free environment, when you feel safe and at ease. This allows for the best digestion and absorption of your meal. In other words, eat when your nervous system is in the *rest-and-digest* or *feed-and-breed* response. Ayurveda provides some guidelines for achieving a stress-free environment.

The Achara Rasayana

The Charaka Samhita is the Sanskrit text on Ayurveda. It is one of the two foundational texts that have survived from ancient India. This pre-2nd century CE text consists of eight books and one hundred twenty chapters. Included in these texts is a code of conduct called the Achara Rasayana whose purpose is to promote mental, physical, social, and spiritual health and worry-free living. Ayurveda says that if you do not follow the Achara Rasayana, nothing else you do, including diet and herbs, will be effective. I have found this to be true in my own life. As I have mentioned before, we start with food, but quickly move to the next layers of mental, emotional, and spiritual digestion in order to arrive at complete healing and reversal of disease.

Review this list on a regular basis to keep the points lively in your awareness.

- Always speak the truth.

- Do not be angry (or at least don't hold onto it).

- Do not drink alcohol.

- Observe monogamy in your sexual relationship.

- Do not be violent.

- Avoid over-exertion.

- Be calm and peaceful in mind.

- Do not hurt others with your speech; speak pleasantly.

- Clean the body by bathing and regular washing.

- Be courageous and patient.

- Donate to those in need.

- Follow religious and virtuous acts according to your own beliefs.

- Respect your teachers, priests, elders, guru, and all animals.

- Do not be cruel to anyone.

- Be merciful to all who are in need of your help.

- Maintain balance in waking and sleeping; do not stay awake long in the night and do not sleep in the daytime.

- Be a knower of place, time, and measures of activities.

- Be a knower of planning; always do everything according to a plan. It is said that failing to plan is planning to fail.

- Avoid super-egoism.

- Maintain good behavior established by the great sages and saints of society.

- Do not be mean-spirited; be generous and share.

- Engage yourself in the pursuit of pure consciousness.

- Respect and serve your elders.

- Respect and serve priests, sages, and saints who serve your spiritual path and God.

- Respect and serve the people who have conquered their senses.

- Keep yourself busy in spiritual activities.

- Continually study new science, advances, research, and philosophies, and utilize them for the benefit of all human beings.

Following a set of guidelines that allows your body's innate intelligence to take over after you have fed it will help you to get the most out of your food. Ayurveda has a series of steps that are recommended with each meal to enhance and optimize the digestion, absorption, and assimilation of your nutrients.

Ayurvedic Body Intelligence Techniques

- Eat in a settled atmosphere and never eat when upset.

- Always sit down to eat and eat only when hungry.

- Avoid ice-cold food and drink.

- Don't talk while chewing and don't eat too slowly or too quickly.

- Eat only if your previous meal is digested.

- Take a few sips of warm water with meals.

- Favor freshly prepared foods.

- Cooked foods are easier to digest.

- Don't heat or cook with honey.

- Don't take milk with your meal.

- Sit quietly for a few minutes after eating.

- Food should please all five senses.

- Put your fork down between bites.

- Walk 100 steps outdoors after each meal and spend at least 30 minutes a day in nature connecting to the planet you live on.

Tips for Mindful Eating

Bringing the practice of mindfulness to your eating experience can help you to reduce cravings, control your portion sizes, and enhance your connection to the people, animals, and nature that contributed to the food on your plate. Here are some tips to enhance your eating experience to make it more nourishing and healing.

1. *Eat in a setting where you feel relaxed.* If you are eating in the car, in front of a computer doing work, or on the phone, you are not able to give full attention to eating, and, as a result, you may tend to eat more or eat foods that are not healing. If you are feeling emotional and are tending towards eating, see if you can first acknowledge and express your emotions rather than eating them. These practices will all help with the digestive process, helping you to get the most out of food.

2. *Eat a palette of colors.* Many people eat a "brown, yellow, and white diet." Instead of lackluster, bland eating, try to sample all the colors of food, including red, orange, yellow, green, and purple, to ensure that you get enough of the important phytochemicals that have health benefits.

   a. **Red:** Red apples, beets, red cabbage, cherries, cranberries, pink grapefruit, red grapes, red peppers, pomegranates, red potatoes, radishes, raspberries, rhubarb, strawberries, tomatoes, watermelon

   b. **Orange:** Apricots, butternut squash, cantaloupe, carrots, mangoes, nectarines, oranges, papayas, peaches, persimmons, pumpkin, tangerines

   c. **Yellow-Green:** Green apples, artichokes, asparagus, avocados, green beans, broccoli, Brussels sprouts, green cabbage, cucumbers, green grapes, honeydew melon, kiwi, lettuce, lemons, limes, green onions, peas, green pepper, spinach, zucchini

   d. **Blue-Purple:** Purple kale, purple cabbage, purple potatoes, eggplant, purple grapes, blueberries, blackberries, boysenberries, marionberries, raisins, figs, plums

3. *Say a prayer of gratitude before eating.* Having appreciation for the source of your food, the earth that provided it, and the people who planted, harvested, and brought it to your table allows you to obtain the most of its vital energy.

4. *Sample a variety of flavors.* When we don't eat all of the variety of flavors at a meal—salty, sweet, bitter, pungent, and savory—we may come away from the meal feeling like we are "missing something," and ultimately, food cravings can result. By getting small amounts of all the flavors of food, a practice common in other cultures such as in Asia, we may feel more fulfilled and desire less food after a meal.

5. *Eat only in an 8-hour window.* When you eat in an 8-hour period of time, you are mirroring the circadian rhythm you are biologically wired to follow. Before we had electricity, we went to bed when it was dark. Eating in front of TV and computer screens is modern man's downfall and a huge reason for our obesity epidemic. Give your digestive system a rest for 16 hours daily. Eat only between 8:00 am and 4:00 pm or 9:00 am and 5:00 pm.

6. *Take 10 deep-belly breaths before you begin eating.* This will help active your "rest and digest" or parasympathetic nervous system, enhancing your digestion and thus your overall health and ability to detox toxins.

7. *Chew thoroughly.* The process of digestion begins in the mouth where enzymes are secreted in saliva to break down food. If we do not properly chew and make our food morsels smaller, we may be subject to indigestion and other digestive problems. The act of eating allows us to be mindful, and in the moment, of our exchange of energy with foods.

Food for Thought

What do you already incorporate from the list above in your eating habits?

_____
_____
_____
_____
_____
_____
_____
_____
_____
_____

What habits of mindfulness would you like to incorporate into your life?

_____
_____
_____
_____
_____
_____
_____
_____
_____
_____
_____

What are the immediate action steps you are committed to taking to incorporate mindfulness into your meal times?

_____
_____
_____
_____
_____
_____
_____
_____
_____
_____
_____

Make Your Relationship with Food a Healthy One

Food addiction is an addiction the same as alcohol or drugs. Most people are not addicted to food, but many don't have a healthy relationship with food. To find out your relationship with food, please answer the following questions:

1. What is your first memory of food?

_____

_____

_____

_____

2. Can you eat when you are hungry and quit when you are satisfied?

_____

_____

_____

_____

3. Do you overeat or under eat compulsively?

_____

_____

_____

_____

4. Do you stop eating because you think you should (as opposed to because your body is satisfied)?

_____

_____

_____

_____

5. Do you have a history of eating disorders? Is there alcoholism in your family?

_____

_____

_____

6. Do you feel that your food selections are a combination of "healthy foods" and "pleasurable food?

_____

_____

_____

_____

7. What is your family's relationship with food?

_____

_____

_____

_____

8. Do you use alcohol or drugs to control your weight?

_____

_____

_____

_____

9. Can you leave some cookies on the plate because you know you can have some tomorrow?

_____

_____

_____

10. Do you usually pick foods based on their calorie content?

_____

_____

_____

_____

11. How often do you eat? Is there anything you eat too little or too much of?

_____

_____

_____

_____

12. Are you or is anyone else concerned about your eating or your weight?

_____

_____

_____

_____

13. Do you become physically uncomfortable (such as weak, tired, dizzy, a headache) when you under-eat or diet?

_____

_____

_____

_____

14. Do you trust that if you eat when you are hungry and stop when you are satisfied, you will not get fat?

_____
_____
_____
_____
_____
_____
_____
_____
_____
_____
_____

15. Do you feel guilty when you eat to the point that you are stuffed and uncomfortable?

_____
_____
_____
_____
_____
_____
_____
_____
_____
_____
_____

16. Can you balance the time you give to thoughts about food, weight, and dieting with other important aspects of your life, such as relationships, work, and self-development?

_____
_____
_____
_____
_____
_____
_____
_____
_____
_____
_____

Am I a Food Addict?

The following questions come from the Food Addicts Anonymous Site. To find out if you have a food dependency problem, answer the following questions as honestly as you can.

1. Have you ever wanted to stop eating and found you couldn't?

2. Do you think about food or your weight constantly?

3. Do you find yourself attempting one diet or food plan after another, with no lasting success?

4. Do you binge and then "get rid of the binge" through vomiting, exercise, laxatives, or other forms of purging? Do you eat differently in private than you do in front of other people?

5. Has a doctor or family member ever approached you with concern about your eating habits or weight?

6. Do you eat large quantities of food at one time (binge)?

7. Is your weight problem due to your "nibbling" all day long? Do you eat to escape from your feelings?

8. Do you eat when you're not hungry?

9. Have you ever discarded food, only to retrieve and eat it later? Do you eat in secret?

10. Do you fast or severely restrict your food intake? Have you ever stolen other people's food?

11. Have you ever hidden food to make sure you have "enough"?

12. Do you feel driven to exercise excessively to control your weight?

13. Do you obsessively calculate the calories you've burned against the calories you've eaten? Do you frequently feel guilty or ashamed about what you've eaten?

14. Are you waiting for your life to begin "when you lose the weight"? Do you feel hopeless about your relationship with food?

If you answered yes to any of the above questions, then you may be a food addict. You are not alone. FA offers hope through a real solution to food addiction. Go to a meeting and find a sponsor, or call an FA member. The member will help you find a sponsor who will guide you and help you begin the FA program: fa@foodaddicts.org.

Make Your Relationship with Your Body a Healthy One

When you hate your body and the way it looks, you are more likely to have an unhealthy relationship with food. Not only that, but your body will believe you when you send it negative messages. Think of what happens to a small child that is abused. He or she begins to believe they are worthless. Your body responds in much the same way as an abused child when it is abused. It's important to send your body messages of gratitude and appreciation consistently. Your cells will respond by behaving in more vibrant ways, just like a flower that has been deprived of sunlight and water will immediately turn its face to the light when it gets an opportunity. Love is medicine. It's the best medicine there is. Your body needs you to love it if it's going to carry you through this life with the strength and stamina you require to live your purpose.

When I take people on retreat, I often use this simple exercise to help them move into a more collaborative and gracious relationship with their bodies. In the space below, draw a picture of yourself and list at least 10 things you love about your body next to your picture. It's usually easier, for women especially, to find what they don't like about their bodies. You can write only one thing you would like to improve. The rest of the list needs to include all of what you can admire about your lovely body. Examples I use for myself: I love my smile, my eyes, my teeth, my strong heart, my strong legs, my nose, my mind, my feet, my hands, and my ankles. Now you try . . .

SECTION 4

Autoimmune Cooking Basics

CHAPTER NINE

The Essentials

*"When diet is wrong, medicine is of no use.
When diet is correct, medicine is of no need."*

—*Ayurvedic proverb*

Why this Cookbook?

It is a pleasure to offer you these recipes, a compilation of my favorite gluten-free, sugar-free, and dairy-free recipes. Like most of my patients, I have little time to spend standing in a kitchen preparing nourishing food for myself and my family. But necessity is the mother of invention, and I have spent the last several years creating efficient ways to meet my family's nutritional needs. You are holding the result.

Many of my patients look like a deer caught in the headlights when I say something like, "Look online for paleo recipes. You will find hundreds of them." Not everyone is a culinary adventurer. So I created recipe templates for my patients that I am sharing with you in this book. By the way, don't be intimidated by the word, "templates." A template in this case is just a simple way to organize the recipe to allow you to see food categories, usual ingredients, and options to customize the recipe to your likes and dietary needs. For instance, here is the template for the master recipe for cookies you'll find in the *Guilt-Free Easy Desserts* Chapter.

Food Categories	Ingredients	Make it Your Own
Sweetener	1 cup coconut sugar	1 cup lo han or monk fruit, 1 cooked sweet potato, 1 banana
Protein (optional)	6 tablespoons Great Lakes green label collagen	1 scoop protein powder
Binder	1 egg whisked	One tablespoon flax seeds and three tablespoons of water to replace one egg
Fat	1 cup almond butter	Other nut or seed butter or coconut oil or ghee or palm shortening
Other	½ teaspoon baking soda	½ teaspoon baking soda=1 teaspoon apple cider vinegar
Spice	Pinch sea salt	Cinnamon, nutmeg, ginger
Flavoring	½ cup Lily's chocolate chips 1 teaspoon vanilla	Nuts, raisins, almond flavoring, ½ cup raw cacao powder, ½ cup unsweetened shredded coconut, ½ cup pureed pumpkin.

Why do I present recipes in this template format? Many years ago, when I worked in the intensive care unit (ICU) in a hospital, I taught nurses the high-tech knowledge they needed to work in the ICU. Yet having lived through a power outage in a hospital ICU, I knew that to rely on technology was a mistake. When I was caring for a patient who had just returned from the operating room after undergoing open heart surgery, the power AND the generator failed in the ICU. Because I understood the basic physiology and framework of the human body and how the drugs we were using biochemically interacted with the body, I was able to keep my patient alive for an hour without the high-tech equipment we usually rely on while the power was being restored. This was a first-hand experience as to why it was more important to understand the framework for why and how the technology worked to monitor a patient's vital statistics. Then, if a monitor failed, a nurse could still dose the necessary medication a patient needed to stay alive if there was a computer failure.

This is what these templates are. I am teaching you the framework or structure for why a recipe works and how to build it into a life-enhancing meal that will fill you with vitality and life force. Each of these templates can be changed to fit your needs and tastes. For example, you might not be able to tolerate nuts. If you can't, there are alternative options offered in the template. If you cannot eat eggs, you are given a way to replace them in the template.

Every person is unique. There is no one diet that will work to reverse inflammation and autoimmunity or cancer in every single person. I have patients who come to see me who are frustrated after following what they have been told is an autoimmune paleo diet. They are angry because they have spent a lot of money on expensive testing and supplements and strictly followed the protocol their functional medicine provider prescribed for them. I have found that people with autoimmune disease or other inflammatory issues are usually perfectionists and don't know it. They are often self-driven and achievement oriented. In short, they are a typical Type A personality type, or a pitta dosha. When what they are told will work doesn't get them the results they are attached to, they can become frustrated and angry, causing a vicious cycle of even more inflammation.

Like me, you have likely walked the path of moving from the standard American diet (SAD) to a more health-conscious way of eating in order to reverse your own illness, or that of a loved one or child. I know that the transition from a SAD diet to a whole foods way of eating can be tough. That's why this is my gift to you. You are joining me at my table and eating the food my family eats. This cookbook is the answer to the question I hear every day in my clinic, "What do I eat if I stop eating gluten, sugar, soy, dairy, and processed food?" It's also my response to the most common refrain I hear in my office, "If you only knew how overwhelmed I am. I don't have time to cook."

The goal of this book is to help you achieve optimal wellness and vitality. May it bring you great joy as you embark on a journey of food discovery and culinary adventure, moving from an attitude of deprivation to one of abundance and plenty. Most of the recipes have 7 ingredients or less and take less than 30 minutes to prepare. Many of them take 10 minutes or less to

prepare. All of this just takes willingness. Willingness to take care of yourself. Willingness to nourish your body, mind, heart, and spirit. I have taken the guesswork and complicated gourmet creations out of this book. Once you get comfortable with the structure of how to make a stir fry, a crock-pot meal, a salad dressing, a cookie, a muffin, you can start playing with the basic recipe and make it your own with your unique flair. Most of all, have fun!

Some Helpful Tools for Your Kitchen

1. A powerful blender.

2. Non-toxic cookware free of non-stick coatings, such as stainless steel and cast-iron pans.

3. An easy-to-clean juicer. I love the Breville juicer. I juice every morning and it's a snap with this juicer.

4. Spiralizer to make your own gluten-free noodles from vegetables.

5. Stainless steel zester for grating lemon, lime, nutmeg, ginger, and turmeric.

6. Stainless steel measuring cups and spoons.

7. Glass mixing and storage bowls.

8. Coffee grinder to grind spices.

9. Quart-sized glass jars for infusions, teas, and ferments.

10. Bamboo or glass lids for making sole solutions in jars.

11. Glass teapot with infuser.

12. Food processor if desired. I usually use my blender.

13. A pizza stone is totally optional but a lot of fun to have if you make pizzas.

14. Parchment paper.

Pantry Items: Buy Organic/Local and Biodynamic Where Possible

Fats/oils:

- Extra virgin olive oil
- Walnut oil
- Grapeseed oil
- Avocado oil
- Coconut oil
- Sesame oil
- Ghee
- Coconut milk (canned, full fat)
- Creamed coconut
- Coconut flakes
- Sacha Inchi oil
- Hemp oil
- Brazil nut oil

Seeds/Seed Butters:

- Raw pumpkin seeds
- Raw sunflower
- Flaxseeds (buy whole, grind in a coffee grounder)
- Raw pumpkin seed butter
- Raw sunflower seed butter
- Raw tahini

- Chia seeds
- Hemp heart

Raw Nuts/Nut Butters:

- Walnuts
- Almonds
- Pecans
- Pistachios
- Peanuts
- Cashews
- Hazelnuts
- Chestnuts
- Brazil
- Nut butter
- Sacha nuts

Sweets:

- Goji berries
- Golden berries
- Mulberry
- Raw cacao powder
- Cacao nibs
- Stevia
- Raw local honey
- Dates
- Coconut nectar or crystals
- Yacon syrup
- Monk fruit

- Xylitol

Spices/Flavorings:

- Primal Kitchen Mayo with Avocado Oil
- Coconut aminos
- Raw apple cider vinegar
- Sea salt
- Ginger
- Cinnamon
- Cardamom
- Turmeric
- Cumin
- Garlic
- Herbamare
- Alioli
- Tapenades
- Chicken paste

Vegetables and Herbs: (Eat a variety of colors)

- Salad greens
- Cucumber
- Red, orange, and yellow peppers
- Avocado
- Onion
- Broccoli
- Brussel sprouts

- Cauliflower
- Leafy greens such as spinach, chard, kale, and collard greens
- Tomatoes
- Sugar snap peas
- Zucchini
- Spaghetti squash
- Cilantro
- Parsley
- Oregano

Fruits:

- Blueberries
- Strawberries
- Grapes
- Apples
- Citrus fruits
- Pears
- Cherries
- Blackberries
- Mangos
- Cranberries

Starchy Vegetables:

- Sweet potato
- Butternut squash
- Pumpkin
- Acorn squash

- Beets
- Carrots
- Peas

Protein:

- Lean chicken, turkey
- Red meat: free range grass-fed, local
- Tuna, sardines: wild caught, tinned with no BPA lining
- Salmon
- Halibut
- Trout
- Flounder
- Striped bass
- Pasture raised eggs
- Beans
- Lentils
- Hummus

Fermented Foods:

- Kimchi
- Fermented carrot sticks
- Kombucha
- Yogurt, kefir (plain with no sugar)
- Miso

Herbal Teas:

- Dandelion leaf
- Nettle

- Peppermint
- Ginger
- Chamomile
- Rooibos
- Milk thistle
- Rosehip
- Lemon balm
- Tulsi
- Red raspberry leaf
- Red clover
- Apple cinnamon
- Capomo (Mayan nut coffee substitute)
- Yerba mate
- Chicory
- Vanilla
- Rooibos chai

Powders/smoothie additions:

- Protein powder: Functional Nutrients
- Collagen (Great Lakes from Amazon)
- Hemp heart
- Flaxseed oil (high lignin)
- Pumpkin seed protein powder
- Ground turmeric
- Ground cinnamon
- Ground ginger
- Raw cacao powder
- Maca root powder

- Spirulina powder
- Chlorella powder

Broths:

- Homemade bone broth
- Kale chips
- Bars made from free range, organic ingredients
- Paleo Wraps
- Huma Chia goo for runners

Flours:

- Almond flour/meal
- Coconut flour
- Hazelnut flour
- Cashew flour
- Tapioca

Thickeners:

- Gelatin (Great Lakes red container)
- Agar (seaweed in the Asian section)

Why You Need to Eat Organic

When you purchase organic food, you are ensuring that your food is free of insecticides, herbicides, and pesticides. These chemicals have been shown to cause diseases such as autoimmunity and cancer.

Again, as I mentioned in Chapter Seven, The Environmental Working Group (EWG) is a fantastic resource for information on how to clean up your home, diet, car, office, and the environment. They list the Dirty Dozen (produce that must be organic) and the Clean Fifteen (lower in chemicals). Go to www.ewg.org to find out more information about cosmetics, cleaning supplies, how to read labels, and much more.

Make sure you buy organic, pastured eggs and animal protein. These animals have been raised more humanely and are free of antibiotics and harmful hormones and chemicals.

The list below from the EWG is in numerical order with the lowest numbers bearing a higher load of pesticides and the higher numbers carrying a lower load.

1. Strawberries
2. Apples
3. Nectarines
4. Peaches
5. Celery
6. Grapes
7. Cherries
8. Spinach
9. Tomatoes
10. Sweet bell peppers
11. Cherry tomatoes
12. Cucumbers
13. Snap peas - imported
14. Blueberries - domestic
15. Potatoes
16. Hot peppers

17. Lettuce

18. Kale / collard greens

19. Blueberries - imported

20. Green beans

21. Plums

22. Pears

23. Raspberries

24. Carrots

25. Winter squash

26. Tangerines

27. Summer squash*

28. Snap peas - domestic

29. Green onions

30. Bananas

31. Oranges

32. Watermelon

33. Broccoli

34. Sweet potatoes

35. Mushrooms

36. Cauliflower

37. Cantaloupe

38. Grapefruit

39. Honeydew melon

40. Eggplant

41. Kiwi

42. Papayas*

43. Mangos

44. Asparagus

45. Onions

46. Sweet peas frozen

47. Cabbage

48. Pineapples

49. Sweet Corn*

50. Avocados

* A small amount of sweet corn, papaya, and summer squash sold in the United States is produced from Genetically Engineered (GE) seed stock. Buy organic varieties of these crops in order to avoid GE produce.

CHAPTER TEN

Medicinal Anti-Inflammatory Foundational Recipes

Dosha-Specific Spice Blends (Churnas)

Your Taste for Life

Ayurveda uses the tastes to balance the doshas. See the chart in figure 5. Which tastes are most prominent in your daily diet? Which tastes do you turn to in times of mental or emotional stress? How can you begin to expand your palate and menu options to include all six tastes? Can you extrapolate that awareness to your tolerance for experiences that span the spectrum of sweet to salty and everything that is included in between?

One of the ways Ayurveda brings a balance of all the tastes to your table is through churnas. What are churnas? Churnas are Ayurvedic spice mixes designed to balance your doshas. (See The Three Body Types or Doshas in Chapter Five.) They help to regulate and keep the body in balance and harmony.

Spices are used liberally in Ayurvedic cooking for good reason. I am often told by my patients who have begun the difficult task of overhauling their diets that food is now "tasteless." Healthy eating that excludes processed foods packed with preservatives, carcinogens, and sugar does not need to be joyless or tasteless. In fact, when you use these churnas, you will find a new joy in culinary adventuring. Not only will your food pop with mouthwatering taste, but your body will thank you for the medicinal qualities these spices offer by lowering inflammation.

Note that there are three different recipes here, one for each dosha type. If you don't know your dosha, you can take a self-assessment on my website here: https://www.drkeesha.com/dosha-assessment/. Use these delicious spice blends during meals, while cooking, or put on snacks and salads. They are a quick and effective way to bring yourself into balance.

In Ayurveda, though spices are used medicinally to balance the doshas, the churnas I have created here for each dosha type are not meant to cure any disease. They are meant to help you experience each of the six tastes the way the ancient people who wrote about and lived Ayurveda did. Have fun with this. Mix your own blends. Pay attention to how your mind feels as you use all six tastes. Are you more capable of noticing your thoughts when you think of them as one of the six tastes? As you sprinkle each churna on your food, do it with mindfulness of your thought patterns and the need for balance.

To make each dosha-specific churna, grind each spice in a spice grinder, with a mortar and pedestal, or in a coffee grinder. Stir to mix and store in glass containers.

Vata Churna

In the fall and winter, especially if you are over 50 years of age or are a vata-predominant person, you might just love this vata churna. If you are any of the other dosha types who are living in cold, dry, windy areas and over 50 years of age and experiencing constipation, trouble focusing, forgetfulness, joint dryness, cracking, and popping, and very dry skin, try this churna and see how it feels to your body and your mind.

2 chili pods ground
2 tablespoons ground cloves
1 tablespoon ground cinnamon
10 cardamom pods ground
4 tablespoons ground coriander
4 tablespoons ground cumin
4 tablespoons black mustard seeds
4 tablespoons ginger powder
4 tablespoons sea salt
4 tablespoons fennel seed powder
4 tablespoons ground black pepper
4 tablespoons garlic powder
4 tablespoons ground nutmeg
4 tablespoons bay leaf powdered
4 tablespoons ground turmeric
4 tablespoons lemon rind granulated

Pitta Churna

This spice blend is great for pitta-predominate persons. You may also benefit from this pitta-balancing churna if you are 20-50 years of age, a "Type A" personality, and it's summer time. Experiment with it and see how you like it. If you are another dosha type 20-50 years of age, living in a hot climate, and feeling like you are inflamed and irritable, try adding this churna to your foods each day. It will help balance the pitta dosha.

½ cup ground coriander
5 tablespoons ground toasted white sesame seeds
5 tablespoons ground cumin
4 tablespoons ground fennel
2 tablespoons ground star anise
2 tablespoons poppy seed powder
2 tablespoons ground nutmeg
4 tablespoons ground toasted coconut flakes
4 tablespoons ground turmeric
½ teaspoon ground saffron
5 cardamom seeds (ground)
2 tablespoons ground peppermint leaves
1 tablespoon ground cinnamon
¼ cup finely granulated sea salt

Kapha Churna

If you are a kapha-predominate dosha type or any other type who is holding some extra weight and water, living in a wet, cold climate, and feeling unmotivated and full of mucous and congestion, try this churna and see how you feel.

¼ cup finely granulated sea salt
¼ cup ginger powder
4 tablespoons caraway seed powder
½ teaspoon clove powder
4 tablespoons fenugreek powder
17 cardamom seeds (ground)

2 teaspoons bay leaves powdered
2 tablespoons coriander powder
4 tablespoons mustard seed powder
4 tablespoons cumin powder
4 tablespoons ground black pepper
1¼ teaspoon ground cinnamon
¼ cup garlic powder
¼ cup onion powder
4 tablespoons ground rosemary
4 tablespoons ground basil
4 tablespoons ground curry powder
4 tablespoons ground turmeric
3 chili pods ground

All-Natural Homemade Vanilla Extract

(Or Lemon, Orange, Coconut, Almond, or Mint Extracts)

You can use the recipe I have included here for vanilla extract with anything. Use your imagination and make your own lemon flavoring by replacing the vanilla beans with the skins of 4-5 lemons, or orange extract by using 5 orange peels. Make your own coconut flavoring by using 1½ cups flaked coconut instead of vanilla beans. Add 4 peeled almonds to the vanilla and make your own almond flavoring. ½ cup fresh mint leaves makes a fresh and minty peppermint extract. They are all delicious and super easy to make.

Ingredients
1 cup vodka
3 vanilla beans

Directions
Place split vanilla beans and vodka in a clean glass bottle. Store 10-12 weeks in a cool, dark place. Remove the beans and begin to use your extract. It's delicious!

Cauliflower Rice

Cauliflower is an amazingly versatile vegetable that is a lot of fun to experiment with. One of my favorite ways to use it is to turn it into "rice." Not only do you avoid the extra starch that regular rice adds to a meal, but cauliflower rice gives you a great way to squeeze more servings of vegetables into your day.

There are two easy ways to make cauliflower rice. You can either use a hand grater traditionally used for shredding cheese, or a food processor to cut it into small "rice like" pieces quickly.

When the cauliflower is grated, press any excess moisture using an absorbent dish towel to squeeze out any remaining water.

Paleo Pasta

Spaghetti Squash Pasta

Ingredients
1 spaghetti squash
Olive oil
½ teaspoon salt
¼ teaspoon black pepper

Instructions
Preheat oven to 400°F. Cut the spaghetti squash in half lengthwise and put face down in baking dish in 1 inch of water. Bake until squash has softened enough to scoop out (about 25-35 min). You can test it by sticking back of squash with a fork and it should be soft. When finished, pull the "noodles" from the skin with a fork and toss with olive oil, sea salt, and pepper.

Zoodles-Zucchini Pasta

Zucchini pasta is versatile and delicious. It makes a great base for sauces and salads of all kinds. The great thing about zoodles is you don't have to cook them, you just heat them up to achieve the perfect al dente noodle. There are several ways to make zoodles.

Using a Spiralizer: Creates curls of your favorite vegetables in seconds. Just wash a zucchini, cut off both of the ends, place it next to the blade and spin. In a few seconds the whole zucchini is spiral sliced.

Using a Julienne Peeler: You likely have one of these in your kitchen already. A julienne peeler is a vegetable peeler with another side that juliennes vegetables.

Using a Mandolin: The mandolin creates slightly thicker zoodles than a peeler does in about half the time. The blades are really sharp on a mandolin, so you must use the plastic holder and be very careful.

Bone Broth

Why Broth?

Broth or stock is an infusion rich in minerals that is made from the bones of healthy animals boiled in water with herbs, spices, and veggies. Bone broth is what is known as a traditional or healing food that was made by our grandparents, great grandparents, and so on. Bone broth is nutrient dense and inexpensive to make.

It's a win-win because it helps to heal leaky gut and balance chaotic hormones. This highly nutritious broth is high in phosphorous, magnesium, and calcium, so it's amazing for anyone who needs to heal their digestive system, joints, hair, nails, and skin. I have seen this get rid of cellulite in my own body.

My Recipe for Bone Broth

I eat a roasted chicken or turkey every week. I save that carcass in the freezer if I am not planning on making broth right away. Sometimes I will save up 2 chicken carcasses to make my broth so I get twice as much in one session and then freeze it.

You can also go to your local butcher to get bones.

Ingredients

Chicken or turkey carcass or 2
    pounds of bones
2-3 carrots
1 yam or sweet potato
3 garlic cloves
1 onion
2-3 celery stalks
2 tablespoons apple cider vinegar
Herbs: 1 tablespoon sea salt, 2
    teaspoons black pepper, 1 bunch of
    parsley, 2 sprigs of rosemary and
    1 bunch of sage

Directions

Add the bones to a stock pot with the water and add the vinegar. Let them soak for 30 minutes. Then add your veggies and herbs and simmer for the following times for each kind of bones:

- Beef: 48 hours
- Chicken or poultry: 24 hours
- Fish: 8 hours

When finished, remove from heat and allow to cool somewhat. Strain using a metal strainer to remove the bones and veggie chunks.

Store in glass containers for 4 to 5 days or freeze for later.

Golden Ghee

Ghee is another name for clarified butter and is a traditional healing food in India. It is made by heating butter until it liquefies into a golden liquid and the water and milk solids are removed, making it suitable for those who are lactose intolerant.

Ghee contains a combination of saturated and unsaturated fats. About two-thirds of its fat content is saturated, and one third is mono- and polyunsaturated. Of the saturated fat content, most of it is of the short-chained variety, making it easily digestible. Ghee also contains antioxidants, conjugated linoleic acid, and fat-soluble vitamins A, D, E, and K. Try dropping a couple of drops of warm liquid ghee into your eyes at night to strengthen your ocular nerves, clear up dry eye, and moisturize the tender skin around your eyes. Ghee also helps your body absorb herbs when you are taking them for therapeutic purposes.

Ghee has been used in Ayurvedic medicine for centuries for numerous health benefits that range from strengthening bones and digestion to reducing inflammation and weight loss. People that are predominantly vata-dosha types need more ghee than those who are predominantly kapha in nature. I often get asked if ghee goes bad. The answer is no, if you make it and store it properly. Ghee does not need to be refrigerated, but it will grow mold if you dip a utensil contaminated by food into it. In India it is said that "old is gold" when it comes to ghee. In fact, when a baby is born, traditionally a crock of ghee is made and put in a cool dark place for storage. When that child grows up and gets married, the crock of "birth ghee" is given as a wedding present.

Ingredients
2 pounds organic unsalted butter

Directions
Melt the butter in a heavy-bottomed pot over medium-low heat and once it is liquified, turn to low heat. Do not stir. Cook until it is a clear, golden liquid. It may bubble some, and a foam may form on top, but if you have a deep pot it won't boil over. Do not skim off the foam. Golden or light brown solids will form at the bottom. Do not stir these.

Remove from heat while the liquid is still a clear gold but steam has completely stopped evaporating from the simmering butter. If there is still water content in the ghee, it can spoil and won't last indefinitely, so getting all the water out is important. My husband holds his eye glasses over the top of the cooking butter to see if they fog up. When they no longer fog at all, you are done cooking. Note that if you continue cooking after all water has evaporated, the temperature of the ghee increases rapidly and will soon burn. It's a fine line: cook till there is no more water content, but not much more than that. Then you'll have perfect, beautiful ghee that will be the envy of expert chefs!

Remove from heat and pour through cheese cloth (pouring through a paper towel or a coffee filter works nearly as well, just a little slower) into a wide-mouthed glass jar. Cool and then cover with a tight-fitting lid.

Ghee does not need to be refrigerated. Always use a clean utensil to scoop out ghee for use. As long as you don't introduce other foods into your beautiful ghee it won't ever go bad.

Dr. Keesha's favorite variation

Herbed Ghee

Ingredients
- ½ cup soft ghee
- 1 teaspoon finely chopped thyme
- 1 teaspoon finely chopped rosemary
- ½ teaspoon finely chopped sage
- 2 teaspoons finely chopped chives
- 2 teaspoons finely chopped parsley
- 1 clove garlic finely chopped
- ½ -1 teaspoon sea salt

Directions
Add ingredients to room temperature ghee and mix completely. I use my blender to do the mixing and chopping. Serve on my delicious paleo crackers or on top of a stack of paleo pancakes.

Nut and Seed Milk

Up to three-fourths of the world is lactose intolerant. Does that mean you have to give up milk? No! You can make your own milk from seeds or nuts. My personal favorite is sesame seed milk, which has more calcium than cow's milk. Sesame seeds just don't have the marketing team that the dairy industry does. Sesame seed milk is also rich in magnesium, a mineral that is essential for calcium absorption. That's why sesame milk is so much better than cow's milk.

Many people drink almond, rice, or hemp milk from cartons purchased in a grocery store. These manufactured nut milks usually contain inflammation-promoting additives such as carrageenan. Once you make your own homemade milk, you will never go back to store-bought milk again. Not only is it fresh and delicious, but it's a cinch to make.

You can replace the sesame seeds in this recipe with any other seeds or nuts that you tolerate.

Homemade Sesame Seed Milk

Ingredients
1 cup raw sesame seeds soaked overnight
4 cups water
2 pitted Medjool dates or liquid stevia to taste (optional)
½ teaspoon homemade vanilla extract
¼ teaspoon ground cinnamon
1/8 teaspoons ground nutmeg
small pinch sea salt

Directions
Rinse and drain soaked sesame seeds. Then add the seeds, water, pitted dates, and chopped vanilla bean to a blender and blend on the highest speed for 1 minute.

Use a nut-milk bag or large piece of muslin and pour the seed mixture through the bag and into a wide-mouthed pitcher or bowl. Gently squeeze the bag as you go and be patient.

Add the salt, cinnamon, and nutmeg and stir. Store in the fridge for up to 4 days. Shake or stir before drinking, as the milk will separate. So much better for you than store-bought and a thousand times tastier! Drink cold with my favorite paleo brownies or pumpkin chocolate-chip muffins or pour over the top of your paleo cereal or granola.

Creamy Instant Pot Coconut Milk Yogurt

I now make my coconut milk yogurt in my Instant Pot. It's quick and easy and the yogurt is super tasty and creamy. Alternatively, you can also use a yogurt maker. I use the Flora Boost probiotic from Functional Nutrients on www.DrKeesha.com as my starter, as it's dairy free. Once you have a good culture going, you can reserve ¼ cup and use it for your next batch of yogurt and avoid having to use a probiotic or yogurt culture after you make your first batch.

Ingredients
3 cans full-fat coconut milk with the cream separated from the water
1 teaspoon grass fed beef gelatin (or 1 tablespoon agar agar flakes for a vegan version)- I like Great Lakes green label collagen
1 tablespoon maple syrup
2 teaspoons probiotic powder

Instructions
Make sure your Instant Pot liner is clean before starting. Open your coconut milk cans and scoop the cream off of the top, discarding the water. Place the coconut cream into your Instant Pot liner with your gelatin or agar flakes.

Push the yogurt button after closing the pot and allow the coconut milk to boil. When the boil function is complete, your Instant Pot will show "yogurt" on the screen. (I have had a mixed experience with the boil function on my pot. Sometimes it won't come to a boil and I have to remove the lid and use the sauté function to bring the milk to a boil.)

Open your Instant Pot, remove the liner, and whisk the now liquid coconut cream until smooth. Use a thermometer to track when your milk temperature drops to between 110 and 115°F. Now you can add your probiotic starter and maple syrup. Whisk and close the lid. Push the "yogurt setting" again and set your timer using the "adjust" button to set your fermentation time. I like an 8-hour fermentation time. It's just the right tartness for my taste. However, you can experiment to see what works best for your taste.

When your Instant Pot alerts you that fermentation is complete, pour it into sterilized pint-sized glass jars, place lids on them, and chill in the fridge. Each brand of gelatin is different. If your yogurt turns to gelatin in the fridge, cut back on your collagen powder with your next batch.

Serve with fruit, paleo granola, or enjoy by itself.

Ayurvedic Detox Tea

This tea is for detoxification and is lovely to drink in the fall, winter, or spring, when you want your extra weight to melt off as the temperatures are dropping, the rain and snow are falling, or the snows are melting off.

Ingredients

¼ teaspoon coriander seed
¼ teaspoon cumin
¼ teaspoon fennel seeds
1-inch piece of fresh ginger crushed
½-inch piece of fresh turmeric crushed
Juice of ½ lime or lemon

Directions

Add the whole cumin, coriander, and fennel seeds to 1½ cups of boiling water. Crush the ginger and turmeric root in a mortar and pestle and add to water. Simmer for 10-15 minutes. Remove from heat.

Allow the spices to steep for 10 minutes or until cool enough to drink.

Strain the spices out and add the juice of ½ lime or lemon. Drink and enjoy, knowing you are building fire in your digestive system to enhance your metabolism and reduce inflammation. Great for detoxification, loss of excess water weight, and getting rid of mucous.

Sole Solution

I want to focus for a moment on your adrenal glands. These champion glands sit on top of your kidneys and respond to stress for you. Over time they tend to get a bit too jazzed up and then worn down. It's the most common problem I see in women (and men) in my clinic. I always test for adrenal and hormone imbalances. You must test and not guess before taking adrenal supplements.

But there is one easy little thing you can do each morning that helps your adrenals out. Your adrenal glands are in charge of your fluid balance. Giving them a little salt and mineral solution can be helpful. This solution is called sole solution. It's easy to make and a little goes a long way.

Here are some benefits of using sole each day:

- Helps hydration
- Helps with detoxification
- Boosts energy
- Improves digestion
- Helps with blood sugar
- A natural antihistamine
- Helps with muscle cramps

- Bone health
- Healthy veins
- Blood pressure
- Weight loss
- Healthy skin, hair and nails

How to make a sole solution

Fill a glass jar about ¼ of the way with Himalayan Salt, Real Salt, or Celtic Salt (or a mixture of the three). Add water, leaving an inch at the top, and cover with a glass or plastic lid and shake the jar gently. Leave it out on the counter overnight to let the salt dissolve.

The next day, if there is still some salt on the bottom of the jar, the Sole is ready to use. If all of the salt is absorbed, add more salt and continue doing so each day until some remains. This means that the water is fully saturated with the salt.

Mix 1 teaspoon of the sole into a glass of water and drink every morning on an empty stomach. Enjoy the benefits and don't overdo it or you could get a nasty detox headache.

Zesty Guacamole

Ingredients

- 3 Avocados, pitted
- 1 onion, diced
- 2 tomatoes, diced (optional)
- 4 sprigs fresh cilantro, finely chopped
- Juice of 1 lime
- 1 clove garlic minced
- 1 teaspoon ground cumin
- Cayenne pepper to taste
- Sea salt to taste

Scoop the avocado from the skin. Cut into chunks, place in a large bowl, and mash with a fork. Stir in the onions, tomatoes, spices, and cilantro. Squeeze in the lime juice and stir in salt to taste.

Tip: This recipe is great with my paleo crackers, over salads, with an egg frittata, or as a quick snack with chopped veggies. It's a wonderful source of healthy fat, which is great for reducing inflammation and balancing hormones.

Recipe for a Sound Sleep

Sleep is a foundational element for a healthy immune system, balanced hormones, and strong metabolism. Leptin is a hormone important for weight control and blood sugar balance. It is only one of several hormones that are dependent on the amount of sleep you get each night. If you sleep less than 5 hours, your leptin decreases. If you sleep 8 hours, your leptin increases.

Your liver detoxes at night. Sleep is an essential component of any program aimed at healing the adrenal hormone balance and repairing the systems of the body, from the gut to the brain.

Sleep Hygiene Recipe

- Begin to do what Ayurvedic medicine has advised for 10,000 years. Follow a daily routine that includes going to bed at the same time each night and getting up at the same time each morning. It doesn't matter if it's the weekend or a workday. Set fixed times and stick with it.

- Diet: If you have food allergies or toxicity, you will have a misfiring brain. Do a food sensitivity test to determine if something simple that you are eating frequently is making you snore or creating sleep apnea.

- Sleep apnea: If you are waking up because you can't breathe (or your sleep partner is telling you your breathing stops in the night and you snore like a freight train), get a sleep study done. There are now simple dental appliances that can assist sleep apnea.

- Fix your gut: Bad bugs mean bad sleep. If your gut has an overgrowth of yeast, bacteria, or parasites, you will not get the rest you need. A stool test can show this and treatment can begin so you can get the rest you need.

- Sleep in the dark. Recent studies have indicated that sleeping in darkness provides better rest and that sleeping with light may be correlated with depression.

- Don't turn on the light if you get up to go to the bathroom.

- Don't take naps.

- Get at least 30 minutes of outdoors time (even if it's not sunny).

- Only use your bed for sleep and sex. Don't bring screens to bed and don't watch TV in bed. The blue in your electronic screens interferes with melatonin (sleep hormone) production. Resist sending those last emails or watching a violent movie while in bed. One of the worst barriers to sleep is watching the nightly news.

- If you are not tired after you have gone to bed, get out of bed and go into another room to meditate. Don't turn on the light.

- Avoid caffeine, sugar, marijuana, and alcohol completely. Consuming any of these will create a spike and then a fall in your blood sugar that can wake you up later in the night.

- Even though a nightcap or marijuana may help you relax and fall asleep faster, it'll make the second half of your sleep cycle restless and unsatisfying. Alcohol decreases deep sleep and increases arousals from sleep

- Do not read or do any activity that causes mental stimulation one hour before bedtime. The best activity is meditation or another contemplative exercise, reading a book that is NOT mentally stimulating, and/or sex.

- Try to get rid of thoughts that make you worry. Write them down and then forget about them until the next day.

- Move your body for an hour each and every day.

- Do not eat for the last 3 hours before bedtime.

- Create a bedtime ritual such as Epsom salts bath (soak for 30 minutes with lavender essential oil added to it), rinse in the shower, give yourself a massage with warm sesame oil and rub your feet with coconut oil. Ayurveda recommends you rub your scalp and feet with coconut oil before bedtime to soothe the brain. The soles of the feet contain the matching counterpoints to the organs in your body. Use a body brush and brush skin vigorously before your bath.

- Make sure your bedroom is not only dark, but quiet and cool. An easy way to remember this: it should remind you of a cave. While this may not sound romantic, it seems to work for bats. Bats are champion sleepers. They get about 16 hours of sleep each day. Maybe it's because they sleep in dark, cool caves.

- Use ear plugs if you sleep with someone who snores.

- Keep pets out of your bedroom if they disturb your sleep.

- Write down any notes for things you don't want to forget so they don't wake you up in the night.

- Drink the Ayurvedic Sleep Cocktail listed below or a cup of chamomile tea. Not too much liquid, though, so you don't have to get up to the bathroom.

- Use an essential oil diffuser in your bedroom with lavender oil. Or put lavender oil on a cotton ball in your pillow case.

- Progressive relaxation, restorative yoga, or stretching can calm your body and help prevent leg cramps. No hard exercise for 6 hours before bedtime.

- Do an appreciation and gratitude practice before sleep along with forgiveness work for yourself and anyone else who you need to release for the night.

- Avoid sleeping pills or use them cautiously. Most doctors do not prescribe sleeping pills for periods of more than three weeks because they cause dependency.

- Do not smoke or use nicotine 3 hours before bedtime.

- Get a salivary adrenal and hormone test done to see if your cortisol is spiking during the night or if your progesterone is low. Both will interfere with sleep.

- Supplements and herbs that can be useful (depending on root cause):

- Sleep Soundly Kit (available at https://www.drkeesha.com/shop/sleep-soundly-kit/).

- Calm and Clear (available at https://www.drkeesha.com/shop/calm-and-clear/).

Ayurvedic Sleepy Time Cocktail

- Warm ½ cup homemade almond milk with 1 teaspoon ghee, 5 strands saffron, ¼ teaspoon ground nutmeg, ground cardamom, a couple of drops of homemade vanilla extract, and cinnamon to your taste.

- Whip before drinking.

- Drink 1 hour before bedtime and avoid all electronic screens from that point on until you go to bed.

Autoimmune Recipes for Busy People

CHAPTER 11

Recipes for Immune Balancing on the Run

Now the fun really begins! The following recipes have been put into a Master Template format so you can learn the structure that makes an anti-inflammatory and hormone balancing dish. As I mentioned earlier, each template contains the basic ingredients needed to make the dish. It also includes alternate choices you can use as ingredient swaps in the case of food sensitivities, taste, and desire. The template gives you a chance to learn the basics and then branch out and adventure if you feel the desire to.

The following recipes are ones I use a lot in my own kitchen. Like most of you, I am a very busy person. I tend to eat simply. I make sure I eat at least 10-12 cups of a variety of vegetables a day, healthy fats, 30 grams of fiber, and 70-80 grams of clean protein. If you make this your goal, you will significantly reduce inflammation and prevent, if not reverse, illness. Start your day with freshly juiced vegetables and warm water with lemon instead of caffeine.

Master Recipe for Juices

Directions

Put chopped ingredients through your juicer (not blender). Again, I LOVE my Breville juicer. You can then transfer your vegetable juice to your blender and blend in a protein, oil (if desired), and ground flax seeds. You will get the most micronutrients from your juice if you drink it immediately. If you are trying to lose weight do not juice fruit. Fruit without its fiber is pure sugar.

Food Categories	Ingredients	Make it Your Own
Greens	2 large handfuls mixed organic greens Chard Kale 1 cucumber 1 zucchini 1 bunch cilantro 1 bunch parsley 1 bunch of celery Broccoli stems	Mix and match your greens to your taste and what is in season or available at your farmer's market. Always buy organic.
Other veggies	¼ head of cabbage Red and yellow bell peppers Beets Carrots Cauliflower Lemon Lime	Only use a small amount of carrots and beets as they are high in sugar.
Spice	½ inch fresh ginger root and ½ inch fresh turmeric root	Edible essential oils
Additions for the blender	½ cup organic berries Handful of fresh mint leaves 1 tablespoon ground flax seeds 1 scoop Functional Nutrients Pure and Paleo Protein Powder or 3 tablespoons Great Lakes green label collagen	Fruit increases sugar content.

Mean Green Inflammation Buster

Ingredients

2 large handfuls mixed organic
  greens
3 stalks rainbow chard
1 bunch dino kale
1 cucumber
1 zucchini
1 bunch cilantro
1 bunch parsley
3 stalks celery
2 broccoli stems
1-inch chunk fresh ginger root
1-inch chunk fresh turmeric root
1 lime

Directions

Juice all ingredients, pour into a glass and drink immediately. Repeat every morning, rotating your vegetable choices. This juice is fantastic for detoxifying your liver, kidneys, and clearing your skin. It's rich with anti-inflammatory and anti-oxidant power and packed with energy boosting micronutrients. This is what I drink every morning.

Beetilicious Morning Blend

Ingredients

1 red beet
3 large pomegranates
1 lemon
1-inch fresh ginger root

Directions

Wash all of the ingredients. Slice the top and bottom off the pomegranates. Make 4 vertical deep incisions into the pomegranates with a knife and pull the sections apart gently. Scoop the seeds into a bowl. Cut the beet in half and remove the greens from the top. Juice the seeds, the beet, the greens, the ginger, and the unpeeled lemon. Drink immediately. High in anti-inflammatory and anti-oxidant power.

Sunshine Suzie Juice

Ingredients
6 organic carrots
1-inch fresh ginger root
1-inch fresh turmeric root
1 small clementine

Directions
Wash all ingredients. Juice all ingredients (no need to peel anything), pour into a glass and drink immediately. Popping with vitamin A, vitamin C and anti-oxidant activity, this juice is great for the eyes, skin, immune system, and your energy level. Stir 3 tablespoons Great Lakes green label collagen after you have finished juicing the ingredients to slow down the sugar that is in carrots and clementines.

Master Recipe for Smoothies

Smoothies are a quick and easy way to get full handfuls of organic greens, healthy fats, and extra fiber into your day. I don't add ice to mine. The reason for this comes from the ancient wisdom of Ayurveda. Ice puts out your digestive fire and therefore slows down healthy digestion. Make your smoothies with room temperature liquids year-round and add warming spices in the cold and wet seasons to boost your digestive function.

immediately. If you are trying to lose weight, do not add fruit; use only water for your liquid base, and only add 1 tablespoon of your choice of fat. The addition of maca root can help to balance hormones. Turmeric and ginger root help to reduce inflammation. Ground flax and chia seeds contribute fiber. Cacao nibs not only increases anti-oxidants but also helps to boost metabolism.

Directions
Blend all ingredients in a high-powered blender such as a Vitamix. Serve

Food Categories	Ingredients	Make it Your Own
Protein	1 scoop Functional Nutrients Pure and Paleo Protein Powder 3 tablespoons Great Lakes green label collagen	Use your favorite clean protein source.
Greens	2 large handfuls mixed organic greens 1 cup chopped parsley 1 scoop powdered greens	Use 2 cups of your favorite chopped vegetables, such as carrots, beets, sweet potatoes.
Fat	2 tablespoons MCT oil, coconut oil, high lignin flax oil olive oil, hemp oil, or ground flax or chia seeds	If you prefer, you can use your favorite nut or seed butter, whole seeds or nuts, or ½ organic avocado.
Liquid	2 cups water	Or you can use rice, almond, flax, or coconut milk.

Food Categories	Ingredients	Make it Your Own
Spice	½ inch fresh ginger root and ½ teaspoon ground cinnamon	Edible essential oils, cacao nibs, maca powder, lemon or lime juice, other spices or flavorings or stevia if sweet taste is desired.
Fruit (optional)	½ cup organic berries or tart cherries	Fruit increases sugar content. Pumpkin puree

Strawberry Mint Clean Green Energy Smoothie

Ingredients
- 1 scoop Functional Nutrients Pure and Paleo Protein Powder (Vanilla)
- 3 tablespoons Great Lakes green label collagen
- 2 large handfuls of organic mixed greens
- 4 mint leaves
- 1 tablespoon flax seed
- 2 cups of water
- 4 strawberries

Directions
Blend all ingredients in a high-powered blender such as a Vitamix. Serve immediately.

Master Recipe for Energy Snack Bites

My patients commonly report difficulty in following a healthy food plan when they travel or have an overly busy day. These energy bites are simple to make and are easily frozen for a grab-and-go kind of day. They make great energy-boosting snacks for athletes and for kids who are hungry after school.

Directions

Pulse your choice of the following ingredients in a food processer. Roll into balls in your hand and then dip them in your favorite topping. Store in a covered container in the refrigerator or freezer for later use.

Food Categories	Ingredients	Make it Your Own
Protein	1 scoop Functional Nutrients Pure and Paleo Protein Powder or 3 tablespoons Great Lakes green label collagen	Use your favorite clean protein source or omit entirely.
Nut and seed butter	½ cup almond, cashew, or sunflower seed butter ½ cup pumpkin seed butter	Use organic, raw versions if possible.
Sweetener	3 to 4 tablespoons coconut nectar or Yacon Syrup	Lo han "maple" syrup, stevia
Fat	2 tablespoons MCT oil, coconut oil, high lignin flax oil olive oil, hemp oil, or ground flax or chia seeds	Omit if you are trying to lose weight.
Spices and add-ins	Ground cinnamon, nutmeg, ginger, cardamom, anise, allspice and a pinch of sea salt ½ cup unsweetened finely shredded coconut	Edible essential oils, Lily's mini-chocolate chips, espresso, maca powder, other spices or flavorings
Crunch	1 cup organic ground flax & pumpkin seeds (1:1 ratio) or 1 cup organic sesame and sunflower seed, raw & ground in a 1:1 ratio	½ cup puffed quinoa Raw cacao nibs
Topping (optional)	Roll in unsweetened coconut flakes or sesame seeds.	Powdered raw cacao or cocoa nibs

Mint Tahini Bites

Ingredients
½ cup raw tahini
2 tablespoons sesame seeds
2 tablespoons chia seeds
8 drops mint extract
2 tablespoons coconut nectar
¼ cup Lily's chocolate chips

Directions
Pulse all of the ingredients except the chocolate chips in a food processer. Fold in the chocolate chips by hand. Roll into 1-inch balls by hand. Store in a covered container in the refrigerator or freezer for later use.

Almond Joy Bites

Ingredients
½ cup raw unsalted almond butter
¼ tablespoon unsweetened coconut flakes
2 tablespoons chia seeds
1 teaspoon vanilla extract
2 tablespoons coconut nectar
¼ cup Lily's chocolate chips
Roll in coconut flakes

Directions
Pulse all of the ingredients except the chocolate chips (and coconut flakes you will use for rolling later) in a food processer. Fold in the chocolate chips by hand. Roll into 1-inch balls by hand. Roll in coconut shreds and store in a covered container in the refrigerator or freezer for later use.

Sunshine Chocolate Bites

Ingredients
½ cup raw sun butter
2 tablespoons sesame seeds
2 tablespoons chia seeds
1 teaspoon vanilla extract
2 tablespoons coconut nectar
¼ cup Lily's chocolate chips
Roll in sesame seeds
½ cup Lily's chocolate chips melted for drizzling over the top

Directions
Pulse all of the ingredients except the chocolate chips in a food processor. Fold in the whole chocolate chips by hand (reserving the melted chocolate chips for the end). Roll into 1-inch balls by hand. Melt ½ cup Lily's chocolate chips over low heat on the stove in a pan. Drizzle the melted chocolate over the tops of the energy bites. When cool you can store in a covered container in the refrigerator or freezer for later use.

Almond Butter Chocolate Bites

Ingredients

- ½ cup raw unsalted almond butter
- 2 tablespoons raw cacao
- 2 tablespoons chia seeds
- 1 teaspoon vanilla extract
- 2 tablespoons coconut nectar
- ¼ cup Lily's chocolate chips
- ¼ cup Lily's chocolate chips for rolling the bites in at the end

Directions

Pulse all of the ingredients except the chocolate chips in a food processer. Fold in ¼ cup of the chocolate chips by hand. Roll into 1-inch balls by hand. Roll the bites in the other ¼ cup of chocolate chips and store in a covered container in the refrigerator or freezer for later use.

Master Recipe for Lattes

I live in the Seattle area where coffee is nearly a religion. Getting people to quit coffee for a different choice is tantamount to blasphemy. The Pacific Northwest can be cold and damp, and it's nice to have a hot drink to warm up with. Luckily, I have found a fantastic option for people to use as a swap. It's called capomo. It grows in the same areas of the world as coffee but doesn't have the acidity or caffeine that coffee does; thus it doesn't promote inflammation like coffee. Capomo lends itself well to making lattes of all flavors.

Directions

Ground capomo ought to be simmered in water before being pressed through a French Press. Simmering it for 10-15 minutes creates a stronger taste profile that more closely matches coffee than it will if you just use a French Press and hot water.

After you have simmered your capomo, mix all of your chosen ingredients in a high-powered blender until frothy. Serve warm in mugs and enjoy!

To brew capomo

French press: Add 2 tablespoons capomo to your French Press. Bring 8-10 ounces of water to a boil. Pour the water over the capomo. Let it steep for 10 minutes and then press. For stronger flavor, put 2 tablespoons capomo in a pan on the stove top and add 8 ounces of water. Simmer for 10-15 minutes. Pour through French Press.

Percolator: Remove cover inside stem and basket. Fill unit with cold water to desired level. Replace percolator stem assembly and insert coffee basket over stem. Add 2 tablespoons capomo to the bottom of the basket. Check indicator light to know when your capomo is ready.

Tea infuser: Add 2 tablespoons capomo to your tea infuser. Bring 8-10 ounces of water to a boil. Pour the water into a mug and then place the infuser filled with capomo in the mug and steep for 10 minutes.

Coffee maker or K-cup device filter: Place 3 tablespoons capomo instead of coffee in your coffee maker or K-cup filter and prepare according to your device's standard instructions.

Cold infusion: Put 2 tablespoons in a pint glass jar and fill almost to the top with water. Cover and let sit overnight. Now you have the beginnings of iced capomo.

Food Categories	Ingredients	Make it Your Own
Liquid	1 cup freshly brewed capomo	Organic white or green tea or chai tea made from scratch, loose leaf and brewed, or organic tea bags steeped
"Milk"	½-¾ cup full fat canned coconut milk, heated	Use any nut or seed milk of your choosing, heated.
Sweetener		Raw honey, coconut nectar, pitted dates, maple syrup, stevia, or lo han to your taste as desired ½ tablespoon of molasses with the pureed pumpkin, ground ginger, ground cloves, and nutmeg spices makes a yummy gingerbread latte.
Spices (optional)	⅛ to ¼ teaspoon vanilla bean, powdered ⅛ to ¼ teaspoon ground ginger ¼ to ½ teaspoon ground cinnamon Pinch of sea salt	You can add turmeric, nutmeg, ginger, cloves, cardamom, anise, lavender, black or long pepper, or any other spice you love. Try a drop of peppermint food-grade essential oil for a mint taste if making a mocha.
Additions (optional)		2 tablespoons raw cacao powder makes it a mocha. ¼ cup pureed pumpkin makes a fall pumpkin treat. Add one egg yolk and you have eggnog. 1 teaspoon MCT or coconut oil 1 tablespoon ghee

Capomo Coconut Milk Spiced Latte

Ingredients

1 cup brewed capomo
3 tablespoons coconut cream
1 teaspoon vanilla extract
1 teaspoon pumpkin pie spice
Pinch of sea salt

Directions

Put 2 tablespoons capomo in a pan on the stove top and add 8 ounces of water. Simmer for 10-15 minutes. Pour through a French Press.

Pour your brewed capomo into a blender. Add 3 tablespoons full fat canned coconut cream, 1 teaspoon vanilla, pinch of salt, and 1 teaspoon pumpkin pie spice to the blender and blend until frothy. Serve warm in mugs and enjoy!

Master Recipe for Fruit-Infused Drinks

Many of my patients report struggling in social settings where alcohol is served. They don't want to be the "only one" not drinking. Some people also enjoy the ritual of pouring a glass of wine to have during or after dinner. An easy and inexpensive way to replace the ritual of alcohol is to replace it with a different ritual that appeals to the senses. Fruit-infused waters fit the bill nicely. They are pretty to look at, fun to create, and fulfill the need for ritual.

In my office during the summer months, we make fruit-infused waters and use a beautiful crystal decanter with a nice silver pour spout to serve them. Cold infusions can be made in canning jars or glass water bottles if you want to take them with you. Many companies now sell fruit-infuser bottles. The trick is to make it beautiful and appealing so that you won't be drawn to soda, caffeinated drinks, and alcoholic drinks.

Directions

Place all ingredients in a clear glass bottle, jar, or decanter. Once prepared, the fruit-infused water can be stored in the refrigerator in an airtight container for up to a week. I add Great Lakes green label collagen powder to mine to add protein.

Food Categories	Ingredients	Make it Your Own
Liquid	Clear filtered water	Ayurveda teaches that carbonated water makes your energy go in the wrong direction, resulting in digestive issues and "air" imbalances such as belching, gas, headaches, memory loss, ringing in the ears, insomnia, joint pain, and skin problems.
Fruit	1 cup organic seasonal fruit. Some of my favorites are: Strawberries, cherries, raspberries, blackberries, blueberries, mangoes, apples, pears, watermelon, kiwi, cantaloupe, honeydew, pomegranate seeds, lemons, limes, oranges, grapefruits, and cucumbers (okay, not a fruit . . .).	Use frozen fruit if fresh is not available.

Food Categories	Ingredients	Make it Your Own
Herbs	3 tablespoons fresh garden herbs, slightly bruised: mint, lemon grass, basil, thyme, cilantro, sage, and lavender.	
Spices (optional)	Ginger, vanilla bean, cinnamon, star anise	Try 1-2 drops of a food grade essential oil to spice it up.

Summer Blackberry Basil Delight

Ingredients
1 cup fresh organic blackberries washed
Fresh basil leaves
Clear filtered water

Sunny Orchard Quencher

Ingredients
1 organic orange peeled and sectioned (or just sliced)
½ cup organic apple washed and sliced
Clear filtered water

Strawberry Blue Refresher

Ingredients
½ cup fresh organic sliced strawberries washed
½ cup fresh organic blueberries washed
Fresh mint leaves
Clear filtered water

Cucumber Cooler

Ingredients
½ cup organic strawberries washed and sliced
½ organic cucumber washed and sliced
Clear filtered water

Master Recipe for Crackers

Many people crave crunchy and salty snacks. Rather than indulging in starchy, fried, and inflammation-causing processed snacks, you can make these healthy alternatives.

Directions

Pre-heat oven to 350°F. Mix flour, egg, and spices in a food processor until a dough is formed.

Roll the dough out to 1/16 inch between 2 pieces of parchment paper. Remove the top piece of parchment paper and place the dough on the bottom sheet of parchment paper on a baking sheet (still on the parchment paper). Cut into squares using a knife or pizza cutter. Brush with melted fat and sprinkle with spices of your choice. Bake 12-14 minutes. This will solve the need for salty and crunchy snacks and are a great replacement for bread or rolls in a meal.

Food Categories	Ingredients	Make it Your Own
"Flour"	2 cups almond flour	½ cup coconut flour 1 cup ground flax meal
Binder	1 large pastured egg	One tablespoon flax seeds and three tablespoons of water to replace one egg
Herbs and spices	Sea salt (1 teaspoon) Garlic powder (1 teaspoon) Onion powder (1 teaspoon) Ground dried rosemary (1 teaspoon)	Basil Thyme Nutritional yeast Sage
Fat	Melted ghee	Melted coconut oil
Crunch (optional)	2 tablespoons sesame seeds	Chia seeds Ground flax seeds Fennel seeds Poppy seeds

Savory Rosemary Salt Crackers

Ingredients

2 cups almond flour
1 large egg
1 teaspoon sea salt
1 teaspoon garlic powder
1 teaspoon onion powder
1 teaspoon dried rosemary
1 teaspoon avocado oil
2 tablespoons sesame seeds for the top
melted ghee to brush on top

Directions

Pre-heat oven to 350°F. Mix flour, egg, and spices in a food processor until a dough is formed.

Roll the dough out to 1/16 inch between 2 pieces of parchment paper. Remove the top piece of parchment paper and place the dough on the bottom sheet of parchment paper on a baking sheet (still on the parchment paper). Cut into squares using a knife or pizza cutter. Brush with melted ghee and sprinkle with extra salt and rosemary and 2 tablespoons sesame seeds. Bake 12-14 minutes.

Savory Rosemary
Salt Crackers

CHAPTER 12

Breakfast for Busy People

When I take someone off of gluten, this means I have removed many of the traditional American breakfast options such as pancakes, waffles, toast, and cereal.

However, all is not lost. The following recipes are healthy alternatives to the traditional breakfast choices that are filled with gluten, sugar, and processed grains.

Master Recipe for Cereals

Most of us grew up on cold cereal with milk. One of my favorites was a bowl of Grape Nuts or Cheerios with milk and a sliced banana. Many of my patients express consternation when I ask them to replace their morning cold cereal with a smoothie or vegetable dish and protein. Ayurvedic medicine talks about the need for proper food combining and advises us to start the day with warm food rather than cold food that can put out the digestive fire. The following template is for making a hearty hot cereal that will start your day out right. The addition of protein is important for blood sugar balance that will take you through your day with consistent energy levels.

Directions
Combine the protein, base, fat, and spice ingredients, including hot liquid (be careful) in your high-powered blender and blend until smooth. Top with your favorite toppings and serve warm. Alternatively, you can mix all ingredients with a spoon in your bowl and serve warm.

Food Categories	Ingredients	Make it Your Own
Protein	1 scoop Functional Nutrients Pure and Paleo Protein Powder or 3 tablespoons Great Lakes green label collagen	Use your favorite clean protein source.
Base	¼ cup ground flax, chia, or hemp seeds	Gluten-free oats or quinoa if you are eating grains
Fat	2 tablespoons MCT oil, coconut oil, high lignin flax oil, hemp oil	If you prefer, you can use your favorite nut or seed butter or whole seeds or nuts or hemp hearts.
Liquid	1 cup coconut milk or seed milk	Or you can use rice, almond, flax, or hemp milk.
Spice	½-inch fresh ginger root grated, pinch of sea salt, ½ teaspoon vanilla, cinnamon, nutmeg, cardamom, allspice to taste	Edible essential oils, cacao nibs, maca powder, unsweetened coconut flakes, other spices or flavorings or stevia or lo han "maple syrup" if sweet taste is desired
Fruit (optional)	½ cup organic berries or dried goji berries or apple	Fruit increases sugar content.

Nourishing Ginger Flax Hot Cereal

Ingredients

1 scoop Functional Nutrients Pure
    and Paleo Vanilla Protein Powder
3 tablespoons Great Lakes collagen
¼ cup ground flax
1 cup coconut milk
1 inch chunk fresh ginger grated
1 teaspoon cinnamon
½ teaspoon nutmeg
¼ teaspoon ground cardamom
½ cup fresh organic blueberries for
    the top
Lo Han "maple syrup" or stevia if
    desired for sweetening

Directions

Combine the collagen, protein powder, ground flax seeds, spices. Warm 1 cup coconut milk in a saucepan over medium heat. When it comes to a boil remove from heat and add dry ingredients. Pour into a bowl and top with fresh blueberries and lo han maple syrup to sweeten if desired. Serve warm.

Master Recipe for Granola

This easy-to-make granola is a great replacement for cold cereal if you can't go without it. It also makes a delicious topping for the creamy coconut yogurt, frozen dessert, or just eat it straight as an energy-boosting snack.

Directions

Soak your nuts and seeds overnight for the best nutritional absorption and assimilation. Rinse and drain and pat dry. Spread out on a cookie sheet to dry. Combine all ingredients and transfer to a large baking sheet. Bake at the lowest oven setting and turn every 10-15 minutes so it doesn't burn. Cook for 1½ hours or until crisp and slightly browned.

Food Categories	Ingredients	Make it Your Own
Nuts and seeds	4 cups of your favorite raw, organic seeds and nuts	Almonds, cashews, hazel nuts, pecans, brazil nuts, walnuts, pumpkin seeds, flax seeds, sesame seeds, sunflower seeds
Add-ins	2 cups unsweetened coconut flakes, goji berries, hemp hearts	Dried fruit is optional but will add extra unneeded sugar.
Fat	⅔ cup melted coconut oil or ghee	Or you can use avocado or walnut oil.
Spices	½-inch fresh ginger root grated, ¼ teaspoon sea salt and 1 teaspoon ground cinnamon	Edible essential oils, cacao nibs, nutmeg, cardamom

Grain-Free Granola

Ingredients

2 cups raw unsalted almonds
1 cup raw unsalted pumpkin seeds
1 cup raw unsalted cashews
2 cups unsweetened coconut flakes
3/4 cup goji berries
2/3 cup melted coconut oil
1 tablespoon ground ginger
1 tablespoon ground cinnamon
1 teaspoon ground nutmeg
1 teaspoon ground cardamom

Directions

Soak the almonds, pumpkin seeds, and cashews separately overnight for the best nutritional absorption and assimilation. Rinse and drain and pat dry. Spread out on a cookie sheet to finish drying. Combine the rest of the ingredients with the soaked nuts and pumpkin seeds and transfer to a large baking sheet. Bake at the lowest oven setting and turn every 10-15 minutes so it doesn't burn. Cook for 1½ hours or until crisp and slightly browned. Serve with nut milk as a cereal, over the top of coconut milk yogurt or eat dry as a snack.

Master Recipe for Pancakes

A tall stack of flapjacks drenched in maple syrup has always been a favorite breakfast choice for Americans. Pancakes made from processed grains and sugar contribute to blood sugar and hormone imbalance as well as inflammation. The following template provides a healthy alternative to old-fashioned pancakes and replaces them with a breakfast that is hearty and healthy.

Directions

Preheat a small pancake or crepe pan with a little ghee or coconut oil over low heat.

Put all of your ingredients (except for the ghee or coconut oil) in your high-powered blender and blend until smooth. If your batter is watery, just add more of your "flour."

Pour a scant ¼ cup of the batter into your pre-heated pan on the stove top. When your pancake begins to get small bubbles on the top, it's time to turn it over and cook until golden on the other side. Continue until you have used all of your batter.

Serve with fresh berries, lo han "maple syrup," and with whipped coconut cream on top and chopped nuts or seeds to garnish if desired.

These freeze well. I have been known to make 50-60 at a time and freeze them for when I need to serve up a quick breakfast. They can be re-warmed in a toaster, oven, or stovetop.

Food Categories	Ingredients	Make it Your Own
"Flour"	2 cups blanched almond flour (not almond meal) 1 cup tapioca flour or arrowroot flour 6 tablespoons coconut flour	1 cup lo han or monk fruit, 1 cooked sweet potato, 1 banana
Liquid	1 cup full-fat canned coconut milk	Use your favorite nut or seed milk.
Binder	6 pastured eggs	One tablespoon flax seeds and three tablespoons of water to replace one egg.
Fat	Ghee or coconut oil to cook the pancakes in on the stove top	½ cup nut or seed butter can be added for an extra hearty pancake.
Other	2 teaspoons baking soda	½ teaspoon baking soda= 1 teaspoon apple cider vinegar

Food Categories	Ingredients	Make it Your Own
Spice	Pinch sea salt	Cinnamon, nutmeg, ginger
Flavoring	1 teaspoon vanilla	½ cup Lily's chocolate chips
		½ cup blueberries
		1 mashed ripe banana
		Chopped nuts
		4 tablespoons cup raw cacao powder
		½ cup unsweetened shredded coconut
		6 tablespoons pureed pumpkin

Perfect Paleo Pancakes

Ingredients
1½ cups blanched almond flour
1 cup tapioca flour
6 tablespoons coconut flour
1 cup lo han "maple syrup"
6 pastured eggs
2 teaspoons baking soda
Pinch of sea salt
½ teaspoon cinnamon
¼ teaspoon nutmeg
½ teaspoon ground ginger
1 teaspoon vanilla

Directions
Preheat a small pancake or crepe pan with a little coconut oil over low heat.

Put all of your ingredients (except for the ghee or coconut oil) in your high-powered blender and blend until smooth. If your batter is watery, just add more coconut flour, 1 teaspoon at a time.

Pour a scant ¼ cup of the batter into your pre-heated pan on the stove top. When your pancake begins to get small bubbles on the top, it's time to turn it over and cook until golden on the other side. Continue until you have used all of your batter.

Serve with fresh berries, lo han "maple syrup," and with whipped coconut cream on top and chopped nuts or seeds to garnish if desired.

Master Recipe for Muffins

Muffins make a wonderful grab-and-go breakfast or snack option. They are easy and fast to make and freeze well for travel or hungry kids after school.

Directions
Line muffin tin with silpat muffin cups and pre-heat oven to 350°F. Combine all ingredients and mix well. Pour into muffin cups and bake for 20 to 25 minutes or until tooth pick comes out clean. Cool for 10 minutes before moving to a cooling rack.

Food Categories	Ingredients	Make it Your Own
"Flour"	½ cup coconut flour or ¾ cup almond flour	¼ cup coconut flour if batter is too stiff
Other	1 teaspoon baking soda 1 teaspoon baking powder	½ teaspoon baking soda= 1 teaspoon apple cider vinegar
Binder	4 pastured eggs whisked	One tablespoon flax seeds and three tablespoons of water to replace one egg
Fat	3 tablespoons melted coconut oil ½ cup almond butter or cashew butter	3 tablespoons melted ghee ½ cup other nut or seed butter
Sweetener	⅓ cup lo han or monk fruit "maple" syrup	4 mashed bananas, 1 cup apple sauce, 1 baked sweet potato
Spice	1 teaspoon vanilla Pinch of sea salt	Cinnamon, ginger grated, nutmeg, blue berries, chopped nuts, currants, poppy seeds
Flavoring	½ cup Lily's chocolate chips	Espresso, raw cocoa powder, lemon juice, pureed pumpkin

Lemon Poppy Seed Muffins

Ingredients
½ cup coconut flour
⅓ cup lo han "maple syrup"
3 tablespoons melted coconut oil
4 tablespoons freshly squeezed
  lemon juice
Zest of a whole lemon
1 teaspoon baking soda
1 teaspoon baking powder
4 pastured eggs
1 teaspoon vanilla extract
Pinch of sea salt
2 tablespoons poppy seeds

Directions
Preheat oven to 350°F.

Line muffin tin with silicone muffin cups.

Combine the coconut flour, lo han syrup, melted coconut oil, lemon juice and zest, salt, baking soda, baking powder, eggs, and vanilla in a food processor and mix until smooth. Stir in the poppy seeds. Pour into muffin cups.

Bake until toothpick comes out clean, about 22 to 25 minutes. Cool completely before glazing on a cooling rack.

Glaze Recipe

Ingredients
¼ cup raw cashew butter
2 tablespoons lo han "maple syrup"
2 teaspoons freshly squeezed
  lemon juice
2 tablespoons melted coconut oil
1-3 teaspoons water

Directions
Beat the cashew butter, lo han syrup, melted coconut oil, and lemon juice until smooth. Add water 1 teaspoon at a time if the glaze needs to be thinned. Drizzle over the top of cooled muffins.

Muffins can be stored in an airtight container in the fridge for up to a week.

Autumn Pumpkin Spice Muffins

Ingredients

½ cup coconut flour
½ cup pumpkin puree
⅓ cup lo han "maple syrup"
4 pastured eggs
1 teaspoon baking soda
1 teaspoon baking powder
1 teaspoon raw apple cider vinegar
2 tablespoons pumpkin pie spice
1 teaspoon vanilla extract
Pinch sea salt

Directions

Preheat oven to 350° F.

Line muffin tin with silicone muffin cups.

Combine the coconut flour, lo han syrup, melted coconut oil, salt, baking soda, baking powder, eggs, and vanilla in a food processor and mix until smooth. Pour into muffin cups.

Bake until toothpick comes out clean, about 25 minutes. Cool completely on a cooling rack.

Store the muffins in a sealed container in the fridge for up to one week, or in the freezer for up to 6 months.

Chocolate Chocolate Chip Muffins

Ingredients

¾ cup almond flour
3 tablespoons Great Lakes green label collagen
1½ tablespoons raw cacao
3 tablespoons Lily's chocolate chips
1 teaspoon baking soda
1 teaspoon baking powder
4 pastured eggs
3 tablespoons melted coconut oil
⅓ cup lo han "maple syrup"
Pinch of sea salt
1 teaspoon vanilla extract

Directions

Preheat oven to 350°F.

Line muffin tin with silicone muffin cups.

Combine the almond flour, collagen, lo han syrup, melted coconut oil, raw cacao, salt, baking soda, baking powder, eggs, and vanilla in a food processor and mix until smooth. Fold in the chocolate chips. Pour into muffin cups.

Bake until toothpick comes out clean, about 15-20 minutes. Cool completely on a cooling rack.

Store the muffins in a sealed container in the fridge for up to one week, or in the freezer for up to 6 months.

Master Recipe for Quick Breads

Sometimes people cannot fathom going for the rest of their lives without bread. This quick bread template offers a variety of choices to fulfill a need for bread. They are easy and fast to make and freeze well. I usually have 2 or 3 loaves in my freezer that I can pull out if I have surprise visits from friends or house guests.

Directions

In a food processor or large bowl, combine almond flour and any additional dry ingredients. Mix in salt and baking soda. Add eggs, melted coconut oil, sweetener, and remaining wet ingredients. Finally, fold in remaining additional ingredients.

Transfer batter to a silicone 6½ x 4-inch medium loaf pan and bake at 350°F for 35-40 minutes or until a toothpick inserted into the center comes out clean. Cool on a rack before serving or storing.

Food Categories	Ingredients	Make it Your Own
"Flour"	1¼ cups almond flour	Other nut flour
Binder	2 pastured eggs whisked	One tablespoon flax seeds and three tablespoons of water to replace one egg.
Other	½ teaspoon baking soda	½ teaspoon baking soda= 1 teaspoon apple cider vinegar
Fat	2 tablespoons coconut oil	Palm shortening or ghee
Sweetener	¼ cup lo han or monk fruit "maple" syrup	¼ cup yacon syrup or coconut nectar
Spice	¼ teaspoon sea salt 1 teaspoon vanilla	Cinnamon, nutmeg, ginger, poppy seeds
Flavoring	1 cup Lily's chocolate chips 1 cup pumpkin puree	Raw cacao powder, cranberries, blueberries, chopped nuts, ¾ cup grated zucchini, mashed bananas, lemon juice, raisins

Pumpkin Chocolate Chip Bread

Ingredients

1¼ cups almond flour
2 eggs
½ teaspoon baking soda
2 tablespoons coconut oil
¼ cup lo han "maple syrup"
¼ teaspoon salt
1 teaspoon vanilla
1 teaspoon cinnamon
½ teaspoon nutmeg
½ teaspoon ginger
1 cup pumpkin puree
1 cup Lily's chocolate chips

Directions

In a food processor or large bowl, combine almond flour with the salt and baking soda. Add eggs, melted coconut oil, lo han maple syrup, spices, and pumpkin puree. Finally, fold in chocolate chips.

Transfer batter to a silicone 6½ x 4-inch medium loaf pan and bake at 350°F for 35-40 minutes or until a toothpick inserted into the center comes out clean. Cool on a rack before serving or storing.

Master Recipe for Frittatas

If you can tolerate eggs, these frittatas are another quick and easy breakfast option that can be made ahead and frozen for later. They provide protein and vegetables to the first meal of your day. Because they can be frozen, they make a healthy choice for kids and adults who have to get out the door to school or work early in the morning. Reheating them in a toaster oven is a cinch.

Directions
Preheat oven to 375°F. Grease each cup of the muffin tin with melted ghee or use silicone muffin cup liners.

In a bowl, whisk together the eggs, spices, liquid, onion, meat and veggies. Pour the mixture into each muffin cup. Fill almost to the top. Cook 20 to 22 minutes or until golden and set.

Allow to sit for 5 minutes after removing from the oven. Carefully remove the mini frittatas from their cups and serve warm or freeze for later.

Food Categories	Ingredients	Make it Your Own
Pastured eggs	9 large eggs whisked	
1 cup (total) finely chopped organic vegetables	Broccoli Onion Red bell pepper Diced sun-dried tomatoes	Leafy greens of your choice Any other veggies you love
Liquid-2 tablespoons	Full fat coconut milk	You can use any nut, seed, or rice milk.
Protein-1/2 cup chopped finely	Cooked bacon	Free range chicken Wild caught salmon Ham Other clean protein Goat or sheep feta if you tolerate it
Spices	Sea salt to taste Cracked pepper to taste	Other spices you love

On the Run Single-Serving Frittatas

Ingredients

- ½ cup diced broccoli
- ¼ cup diced onion
- ¼ cup diced red bell pepper
- 6 finely diced sun-dried tomatoes
- 4 slices cooked turkey bacon crumbled
- 9 eggs
- ½ teaspoon sea salt or to taste
- ¼ teaspoon ground black pepper or to taste

Directions

Preheat oven to 375°F. Grease each cup of the muffin tin with melted ghee or use silicone muffin cup liners.

In a bowl, whisk together the eggs, spices, onion, meat and veggies. Pour the mixture into each muffin cup. Fill almost to the top. Cook 20 to 22 minutes or until golden and set.

Allow to sit for 5 minutes after removing from the oven. Carefully remove the mini-frittatas from their cups and serve warm or freeze for later.

CHAPTER 13

Main Dishes in Mere Minutes

When I was first married in my early 20s, I loved experimenting with new dishes in my new kitchen. I tried to make something new every time I prepared a meal. My creativity was expressed through my cooking. Now that I am in my 50s, I am over that. I have raised four children and they have now left home. I am no longer motivated to spend a lot of time in the kitchen, as I express my creativity in other ways. Now, here's what I most commonly resort to for main dishes:

- One of the easiest, quickest, and most versatile dishes is a stir fry.

- One of the friendliest kitchen tools is the crockpot.

- One of the meals that most lends itself to being made in bulk and frozen is soup.

- The meal that my patients report as their favorite is salad.

I have created templates for all four of these meal options that you can play with and alter to your needs and taste.

Master Recipe for Stir-Fry Main Dishes

Directions

Cook garlic and onions in oil in a large skillet or wok on the stovetop until they are clear. Add the chicken (or your meat choice) and cook through, stirring frequently. Stir in the vegetables and spices and cook until crisp tender. Add the fresh leaf herbs and add-ins at the very end. Stir until heated through. Serve over your choice of base. I like to put a bed of organic greens down and then my hot spaghetti squash or cauliflower rice and then top with my veggie mixture. Omit tomatoes (both fire-roasted and sun-dried) if you have inflammatory issues. Serve immediately.

Food Categories	Ingredients	Make it Your Own
Protein	Pastured chicken breasts x 2-chopped into 1-inch pieces	Grass-fed, free range beef or bison Wild caught salmon De-veined shrimp Use your favorite clean protein source.
Chopped organic vegetables	½ cup each of broccoli, cauliflower, red bell peppers, carrots	Use 4 cups of your favorite chopped vegetables.
Fat	2 tablespoons avocado oil	Or use walnut or coconut oil or ghee.
Add-ins (optional)	½ cup pine nuts ½ cup chopped sun dried tomatoes	⅓ cup marinated artichoke hearts 1 can fire-roasted diced tomatoes
Spices	½ cup finely chopped onion 3 tablespoons minced garlic ½ teaspoon sea salt Several leaves of fresh rosemary, sage, thyme, and basil	½ teaspoon freshly grated ginger root ½ teaspoon freshly grated turmeric root ¼ teaspoon black pepper
Base to serve the stir-fry over	Cooked spaghetti squash A bed of mixed greens	Cauliflower rice Quinoa if you eat grains

Chicken Vegetable Stir Fry

Ingredients

2 pastured chicken breasts chopped
   in 1-inch pieces
2 heads of broccoli cut into bite sized
   pieces
1 onion chopped
1 head of cauliflower cut into bite
   sized pieces
1 red bell pepper cut into bite sized
   pieces
2 carrots cut into 1 inch chunks
2 tablespoons avocado oil
Cauliflower rice to serve with the
   stir fry

Directions

Cook the chopped onion in oil in a large skillet or wok on the stovetop until translucent. Add the chicken and cook through, stirring frequently. Add in the carrots and cauliflower and cook for 3 minutes. Next add the broccoli and cook until crisp tender. Add the chopped bell pepper and cook an additional minute or two. Stir until heated through. Serve over cauliflower rice and eat immediately.

Master Recipe for Salads

Ayurveda recommends that all foods be cooked. Vata body types and those with digestive issues especially do not do well with raw vegetables. A workaround, if you absolutely must have salad, is to toss your greens in a wok to wilt them before you build your salad. This adds a bit of warmth and easier digestibility to your salad.

Directions

Wash and pat dry leafy greens. Remove stemmed greens (like kale) from their stems. Tear into bite-sized pieces and place in large salad bowl. Chop the other veggies into bite-sized pieces. Toss with the greens. Mix all of the ingredients together with the salad dressing of your choice from the next recipe template.

Food Categories	Ingredients	Make it Your Own
Base-4 cups	Leafy greens of your choice: Mixed spring greens Shredded cabbage Lettuce Kale Garden herbs	If you are using kale (dino the best), make sure you "massage" it with 1 teaspoon of sea salt and water for 3-4 minutes. Rinse and continue building your salad.
Chopped organic veggies-2 cups total	Cucumbers Carrots Yellow or red bell peppers Radishes Grilled asparagus, peppers and garlic Brussel sprouts Beets (roasted)	Any veggies you like; raw, roasted, sautéed, or wilted
Fats	Chopped avocado drizzled with lime juice	Goat or sheep feta if you are able to tolerate it
Protein (optional)-½ cup chopped into bite size pieces and cooked through	Wild-caught salmon or other clean fish	Free range chicken Free range bison or beef steak De-veined shrimp Other clean protein
Flavorings	Sea salt to taste Cracked pepper to taste	Other spices to your taste Fresh lemon or lime

Food Categories	Ingredients	Make it Your Own

Toppings (optional)	½ cup organic berries
	½ cup chopped nuts
	   or seeds
	Olives
	Sun dried tomatoes
	Marinated artichoke hearts
		Cooked onion slices
		Roasted garlic
		Chopped mango or
		   other fruit
		Cooked bits of bacon
		Guacamole

Herb Fresh Garden Salad

Ingredients

3 cups organic mixed spring greens
8 leaves fresh basil diced
1 organic cucumber quartered and
   sliced
1 organic carrot thinly sliced
1 each organic yellow and red bell
   peppers chopped
1 cup organic cherry tomatoes
½ cup Kalamata olives

Directions

Wash and pat dry leafy greens. Cut the basil into tiny pieces with kitchen shears. Chop the other veggies into bite-sized pieces. Toss everything with the greens. Mix all of the ingredients together and top with a batch of fresh Tahini Lemon Basil Dressing.

Master Recipe for Salad Dressings

Salad dressings found in grocery stores often contain gluten, soy, MSG, and harmful preservatives and additives. There is nothing quite so tasty as a homemade salad dressing made fresh with garden herbs you have picked from your own kitchen pots. Salad dressing made in this way can become a carrier for needed healthy fats.

Directions
Combine all ingredients in your high-powered blender and blend until smooth. Store in the refrigerator for up to 1 week.

Food Categories	Ingredients	Make it Your Own
Base Oil: 3 parts	Extra virgin olive oil	Hemp seed oil Avocado oil Sesame oil Walnut oil Pumpkin seed oil Flax seed oil
Base Acid: 1 part	Lemon juice	Apple cider vinegar Balsamic vinegar Lime juice Orange juice Grapefruit juice
Herbs and spices	Basil Sea salt Garlic Minced onion Parsley	Oregano Thyme Rosemary Sage Cilantro Cracked pepper Grated ginger Chili flakes
Thickener: 1 part	Tahini	Hemp seed butter Almond butter Ground flax seeds Cashew butter

Food Categories	Ingredients	Make it Your Own
Sweetener (optional): 1 part	Stevia	Honey Maple syrup Coconut nectar
Protein (optional)	3 tablespoons Great Lakes green label collagen	

Tahini Lemon Basil Salad Dressing

Ingredients

1 cup extra virgin olive oil

1/3 cup freshly juiced lemon

1 handful fresh basil

1/4 teaspoon sea salt

1/4 teaspoon minced garlic

1/4 teaspoon minced onion

1/2 teaspoon minced fresh parsley

1/3 cup raw tahini

2 drops liquid stevia

3 tablespoons Great Lakes green
   label collagen

Directions

Combine all ingredients in your high-powered blender and blend until smooth. Use immediately or store in the refrigerator for up to 1 week.

Master Recipe for Roasted Veggies

Roasting vegetables is one of the quickest and easiest way to get cooked vegetables of a variety of colors into your diet. Each day when I get home from work, I pull different kinds of vegetables from my refrigerator and begin quickly chopping them into bite-sized pieces. I know I will have a plate of steaming hot, tasty, nutritious vegetables to eat within minutes. After I have popped them into the oven to cook, I turn my attention to what I am going to have for protein. Always make vegetables come first in your planning and you will have a happy body.

Directions

Wash and chop all of your vegetables into bite-sized chunks. If you are using butternut squash, it will need to be peeled (no need for the delicata squash to be peeled). Peel and chop one clove of garlic and one onion. Spread the chopped veggies onto a large baking sheet. Drizzle with oil, sprinkle with spices, and toss until the veggies are coated. Roast in a pre-heated oven at 475°F until all veggies are fork tender and slightly brown at the edges. This usually takes 10-20 minutes, depending on your oven. Serve warm.

Food Categories	Ingredients	Make it Your Own
Vegetables-3-4 cups total	Beets Carrots Sweet potatoes Purple potatoes Parsnips Rutabaga Brussel sprouts Yellow or red bell pepper Zucchini Yellow squash Delicata squash Cubed butternut squash	Any veggies you love
Seasonings-2-3 tablespoons	Mixture of fresh or dried rosemary, sage, thyme, and basil Sea salt Cracked black pepper	Any spices you love Cloves of garlic Coarsely chopped onion Cooked bits of bacon Squeeze of fresh lime over the top
Fat-1-2 tablespoons	Avocado oil	Olive oil Hemp oil Walnut oil Sesame oil Coconut oil

Main Dishes in Mere Minutes   **189**

Easy Oven Roasted Vegetables

Ingredients

1 head of broccoli chopped into bite sized pieces

1 onion chopped into bite sized pieces

1 head of cauliflower chopped into bite sized pieces

1 Delicata squash thinly sliced

1 carrots cut into 1 inch chunks

1 clove of garlic peeled and chopped

1 sprig of rosemary

1 sprig of thyme

3 tablespoons avocado oil

Directions

Wash and slice the delicate squash in half length-wise. Remove the seeds. Slice each half into thin slices. Wash and chop the rest of your vegetables into bite-sized chunks. Peel and chop one clove of garlic and one onion. Spread the chopped veggies, garlic and onion onto a large baking sheet. Drizzle with oil, sprinkle with herbs, and toss until the veggies are coated. Roast in a pre-heated oven at 475°F until all veggies are fork tender and slightly brown at the edges. This usually takes 10-20 minutes, depending on your oven. Serve warm.

Master Recipe for Soups and Stews

One of my favorite meals is a hot bowl of nourishing soup with my homemade crackers and a diced avocado on the side. When I am in the kitchen, I tend to make several dishes at once in large amounts so I can put some away in the freezer for future meals.

Directions

I like to start my soups with a base of my home-made bone broth. My bone broth is absolutely delicious and I have already shared the recipe for it on page 118. Put 4 cups of bone broth in a soup pot over medium heat. In a skillet, cook a sliced onion with 1 tablespoon minced garlic in 1-2 tablespoons avocado oil until the onion is translucent.

Chop your choice of meat into bite-sized pieces and add to the onions and garlic along with your dried spices and sea salt. Cook all the way through. While the meat is cooking, chop your vegetables into 1-inch chunks and add to the bone broth. Cook over medium high heat until they come to a boil. Simmer for 5-10 minutes, or until the veggies are fork tender. Add the meat and any leafy greens and fresh herbs. Remove from heat and cover the pan and let sit for 5 minutes. Stir and serve warm.

Alternatively, you can omit the meat protein and place all cooked veggies, spices, onions, garlic, and collagen in a high-powered blender and blend until you have a creamy soup. You can add full-fat coconut milk for an even creamier texture. For example, this is great for my favorite butternut squash soup, which also includes bone broth, cumin, salt, and pepper.

Another variation from this template is my favorite creamy cauliflower soup. I steam one head of cauliflower in bone broth until it's tender, then add the broth, the cauliflower, collagen, cooked onion, garlic, and some spices to the blender and blend until it's creamy. So easy and it only takes 10 minutes from start to finish!

Food Categories	Ingredients	Make it Your Own
Base liquid: 4 cups	Bone broth	Or use chicken or vegetable stock or water
Chopped organic veggies-2 cups total	Broccoli Cauliflower Carrots Celery Zucchini Yellow squash Butternut squash	Leafy greens of your choice Any other veggies you love
Fat	Avocado oil	Hemp oil Ghee Coconut oil Coconut milk

Food Categories	Ingredients	Make it Your Own
Protein: 1 cup chopped into bite size pieces	Wild caught salmon or other clean fish	Free range chicken Free range bison or beef De-veined shrimp Other clean protein Add 3 tablespoons Great Lakes collagen to your bowl of soup and stir if you don't want meat protein.
Spices	Sea salt to taste Cracked pepper to taste Thyme, marjoram, sage, parsley, basil	Other spices to your taste Fresh lemon or lime
Toppings (optional)	¼ cup pumpkin seeds, pine nuts, or sesame seeds	Cooked bits of bacon Guacamole Fresh herbs chopped

Creamy Cauliflower Curry Soup

Ingredients

4 cups bone broth
1 head organic cauliflower cut into large chunks
1 tablespoons ghee
½ cup onion chopped
1 clove garlic minced
½ teaspoon sea salt
¼ teaspoon cracked black pepper
1 tablespoons of the churna mixture (from this book) of your choice

Directions

Steam the cauliflower in a pan with the bone broth on the stove top until al dente. Add the hot mixture along with all of the rest of the ingredients to a high-powered blender and blend until smooth. Eat with the paleo crackers in this book.

Creamy Cauliflower
Curry Soup

Master Recipe for Paleo Cauliflower Pizza Crust

Before I figured out how to make pizza crust from cauliflower, I thought my pizza days were over forever. I had not eaten pizza for over a decade when I made my first cauliflower crust pizza. Maybe it was because I had not had pizza for so long, or maybe it was because it was delicious, but with the first bite I thought I had died and gone to heaven. I like to make two crusts so I can use one and freeze one for later.

Ingredients
Makes 2
4 heads of organic cauliflower
2 large pastured eggs
3/4 cup soft goat cheese
1 tablespoon minced fresh oregano
1 tablespoon minced fresh basil
1/4 teaspoon red chili flakes
1 teaspoon garlic powder
Pinch of sea salt
Dash of black pepper

Directions
Preheat oven to 400°F.

Pulse raw cauliflower florets in a food processor until it looks like rice. Add to a pan of boiling water and cook for 5 minutes until tender. Strain through a fine strainer. Squeeze all of the water from the cooked cauliflower using a clean dish towel.

Now beat the 2 eggs with the cooked cauliflower, spices, and goat cheese. Line a baking sheet with parchment paper and transfer half of the "dough" onto it. Roll it out to 1/3 to 1/2 inch thick. Do the same with the other half of your dough. Bake at 400°F for 40 minutes or until the edges of the crust are browned and the middle is firm.

Add whatever toppings and sauces you like from the next chart and bake at 400°F for another 10 minutes, or until everything looks cooked through. Remove from oven, slice, and enjoy.

Master Recipe for Paleo Pizza

Ever since I was diagnosed with rheumatoid arthritis when I was 30, I have pretty much stayed away from tomatoes. Even though I have been free of autoimmunity and inflammation for the last 23 years, I still don't eat marinara sauce. You need to check in with your own body and make your decision about night shade vegetables. This class of vegetables includes tomatoes, white potatoes, eggplant, and bell peppers. They are known to cause inflammation in many people.

My pizza is always a dairy-free pesto base with fresh herbs and cooked vegetables. It's absolutely delicious, but tastes nothing like the pizza from my youth.

Directions

Chop and sauté the following veggies in avocado oil until they are firm/tender. I like to brown my sliced onions with the peeled garlic cloves before adding firmer vegetables like broccoli and carrots. Put your softer vegetables in for the last minute of sautéing (red bell peppers, zucchini, yellow squash, and so on).

Spread your favorite sauce on the cooked crust, followed by any raw greens or herbs you are going to use, and then finish with the vegetables. Lastly, add cheese, if you are a cheese eater.

See the instructions for the crust and how to cook the pizza above.

Food Categories	Ingredients	Make it Your Own
Vegetables	Broccoli flowerets Spinach or kale Sliced bell pepper Tomatoes Zucchini Yellow squash Cauliflower flowerets Sliced carrots Diced beets	
Meat (free range, organic, nitrate free)	Chicken	Sausage Pepperoni Ham Canadian bacon Bacon Ground bison

Food Categories	Ingredients	Make it Your Own
Herbs	Basil Oregano Thyme Parsley Green onion Chili flakes Sea salt to taste Cracked pepper to taste	Or any others you love
Condiments	Peeled garlic cloves Sliced onion Diced sun-dried tomatoes Artichoke hearts Olives	Or anything else you love
Pesto Sauce	3 garlic cloves, peeled 2 cups fresh basil leaves ⅓ cup pine nuts ½ cup olive oil 2 tablespoons nutritional yeast (optional, adds flavor similar to parmesan cheese) 1 teaspoon freshly squeezed lemon juice sea salt to taste **Instructions:** Place all ingredients in a strong blender and pulse until the consistency of pesto. Serve right away or store in fridge for up to 1 week.	May use walnuts or cashews in place of pine nuts if desired. May use avocado oil in place of olive oil if desired. If you tolerate dairy, you can add raw parmesan cheese in place of nutritional yeast.

Food Categories	Ingredients	Make it Your Own
Quick and Easy Marinara Sauce	¼ cup oil avocado oil 2 small onions, diced 3 cloves garlic, minced 1 T sea salt 1 T thyme 1 T rosemary 1 T oregano 1 T parsley 2 T monk fruit 6 cups diced fire roasted organic tomatoes (I like Muir Glen) **Instructions:** Heat oil over medium heat. Add onion and garlic and cook until browned. Add remaining ingredients and simmer until sauce is thickened to desired consistency (about 5-7 minutes). Add to blender and blend.	You can use fresh tomatoes if desired. You can substitute any other spices you like.
Cheese	Goat cheese	Sheep Raw Milk if you tolerate it Almond cheese

My favorite pizza is with a pesto sauce base and topped with caramelized onions, garlic cloves, broccoli flowerets, diced zucchini, sliced red bell pepper, Kalamata olives, sun-dried tomatoes, and sprinkled with a little soft goat cheese.

Master Recipe for Slow Cooker Meals

Making friends with my crock pot was a game changer when I was raising four children and attending graduate school and working part time. Again, you can make plenty of food in your crock pot and freeze some for later. I usually serve whatever I make in a crockpot over a bed of fresh organic greens. The heat from the crockpot dish will wilt the greens so they are easier to digest than a raw salad. Sometimes I will put a bed of fresh greens in a bowl and then layer on cooked spaghetti squash and top with the crock pot ingredients.

Directions

Put your choice of meat in a crock pot. Pour the broth, chopped onion and garlic, flavorings and spices over the meat. Cover and cook on high for the designated time below. Take 2 forks and shred the meat. Serve over cauliflower rice, spaghetti squash, a plate of greens, a baked sweet potato, or beside roasted veggies and a salad.

Food Categories	Ingredients	Make it Your Own
Meat	2 pounds free range chicken breasts	2-3 pounds sirloin steak 4 pounds bone in pork shoulder
Liquid	½ cup bone broth 2 tablespoons apple cider vinegar	Or use chicken or beef broth
Flavorings	1 chopped onion 1 clove of garlic peeled and chopped. 1 ½ tablespoon Dijon mustard 1 can tomato paste 1 ½ tablespoon maple syrup (optional)	Omit the tomato paste and peppers if you have any inflammatory issues.
Spices	1 teaspoon sea salt ½ teaspoon black pepper ½ teaspoon smoked paprika ½ teaspoon ground cumin ¼ teaspoon chipotle chili	¼ cup coconut aminos instead of salt
Cook time	5 hours	8-10 hours for beef and pork

Slow Cooker Pulled Chicken

Ingredients

2 pounds pastured chicken breasts
½ cup bone broth
2 tablespoons raw apple cider vineger
1 onion diced
1 clove garlic minced
1½ tablespoons Dijon mustard
1 can tomato paste
1½ tablespoons lo han "maple syrup"
1 teaspoon sea salt
½ teaspoon black pepper
½ teaspoon paprika
½ teaspoon cumin
½ teaspoon chili powder

Directions

Place chicken breasts in crock pot. Pour the broth, chopped onion and garlic, flavorings and spices over the meat. Cover and cook on high for 5 hours. Take 2 forks and shred the meat. Serve over cauliflower rice, spaghetti squash, a plate of greens, a baked sweet potato, or beside roasted veggies and a salad.

Master Recipes for Marinades

Marinades are my ninja trick for creating fantastic main dishes. You can make marinades ahead of time, pour them over your choice of protein and then allow the meat to soak up the marinade in the refrigerator for two days. When it's time to make dinner, all you have to do is pull the baking dish out of the fridge and pop it into the oven. Voila! Dinner is done in 30 minutes.

Directions

Combine all of the ingredients in your high-powered blender and blend until smooth. Pour over your choice of meat and marinade in the refrigerator for 6 hours or overnight (for up to two days). Bake, broil, grill, or sauté until cooked through. The marinade listed below is one I love over wild-caught salmon filets. After I have marinated the salmon overnight, I bake it in a 375°F oven until it flakes with a fork (usually 10 minutes).

Food Categories	Ingredients	Make it Your Own
Base Oil-3 parts	Extra virgin olive oil	Melted ghee or coconut oil Hemp seed oil Avocado oil Sesame oil Walnut oil Pumpkin seed oil Flax seed oil
Base Acid-1 part	Lemon juice	Apple cider vinegar Balsamic vinegar Lime juice Orange juice Grapefruit juice
Herbs and spices	Sea salt (1 teaspoon) Minced garlic (1 tablespoon) Minced onion (1 tablespoon) Cracked pepper (¼ teaspoon) Dijon mustard (2 tablespoons)	Oregano Thyme Rosemary Sage Grated ginger Chili flakes Minced parsley Ground cumin
Flavoring-½ part	Worcestershire sauce (gluten free)	Gluten free tamari

Food Categories	Ingredients	Make it Your Own
Sweetener (optional)-½ part		Honey Maple syrup Coconut nectar
Crunch (optional)	¼ cup sesame seeds	Unsweetened coconut shreds

Seattle Salmon Marinade

Ingredients

3 cups extra virgin cold pressed olive oil

1 cup raw apple cider vinegar

½ cup gluten free Worcestershire sauce

2 tablespoons Dijon mustard

1 tablespoons minced onion

1 clove minced garlic

1 teaspoon sea salt

½ teaspoon cracked black pepper

Directions

Combine all of the ingredients in your high-powered blender and blend until smooth. Pour over a fresh salmon filet and marinade in the refrigerator for 6 hours or overnight (for up to two days). Bake in a 375°F oven until it flakes with a fork.

CHAPTER 14

Guilt-Free Easy Desserts

Master Recipe for Cookies

I am a recovering sugar addict. Sugar acts within me the same way alcohol does in some people. It affects my mood, my brain, and my joint health. I used to make cookies for my kids to have with milk for dessert. Little did I know that I was feeding them the equivalent of rat poison. After I learned more about nutrition and reversed my autoimmune disease, we were a sugar-free household for many years. Then the paleo revolution started and I learned how to modify some of our old family favorites and make them in a healthier way that wouldn't spike my blood sugar and activate my immune response. Play with this recipe template and you too can learn how to create desserts that don't trigger an inflammatory response in your body.

Directions

Preheat oven to 350°F.

Mix almond or sunflower-seed butter and coconut sugar or monk fruit in a bowl. Add egg or egg substitute and beat until smooth. Add ¼ cup of cocoa powder at a time and stir until smooth if you want your cookies to be a chocolate base. Add the baking soda, vanilla, salt, and chocolate chips (optional) and mix well.

Roll 2 tablespoons at a time into round balls. Place on a silpat-lined baking sheet. Use a fork to press the cookies slightly. Bake 10 minutes. Remove from the oven and cool 5-10 minutes on a rack.

Food Categories	Ingredients	Make it Your Own
Sweetener	1 cup coconut sugar	1 cup lo han or monk fruit, 1 cooked sweet potato, 1 banana
Protein (optional)	6 tablespoons Great Lakes green label collagen	1 scoop protein powder
Binder	1 egg whisked	One tablespoon flax seeds and three tablespoons of water to replace one egg

Food Categories	Ingredients	Make it Your Own
Fat	1 cup almond butter	Other nut or seed butter or coconut oil or ghee or palm shortening
Other	½ teaspoon baking soda	½ teaspoon baking soda= 1 teaspoon apple cider vinegar
Spice	Pinch sea salt	Cinnamon, nutmeg, ginger
Flavoring	½ cup Lily' s chocolate chips 1 teaspoon vanilla	Nuts, raisins, almond flavoring, ½ cup raw cacao powder, ½ cup unsweetened shredded coconut, ½ cup pureed pumpkin

Almond Butter Chocolate Chip Cookies

Ingredients
1 cup coconut sugar crystals
6 tablespoons Great Lakes green label collagen
1 pastured egg
1 cup almond flour
½ teaspoon baking soda
Pinch of sea salt
1 teaspoon cinnamon
½ cup Lily's chocolate chips
1 teaspoon vanilla

Directions
Preheat oven to 350°F.

Mix almond butter and coconut sugar in a bowl. Add egg and beat until smooth. Add the baking soda, vanilla, salt, and chocolate chips and mix well.

Roll 2 tablespoons at a time into round balls. Place on a silpat-lined baking sheet. Use a fork to press the cookies slightly. Bake 10 minutes. Remove from the oven and cool 5-10 minutes on a rack.

Almond Butter Chocolate
Chip Cookies

Double Chocolate Cookies

Ingredients

- 1 cup coconut sugar crystals
- 6 tablespoons Great Lakes green label collagen
- 1 pastured egg
- 1 cup almond flour
- ½ teaspoon baking soda
- Pinch of sea salt
- 1 teaspoon cinnamon
- ½ cup Lily's chocolate chips
- ¼ cup raw cacao
- 1 teaspoon vanilla

Directions

Preheat oven to 350°F.

Mix almond butter and coconut sugar in a bowl. Add egg and beat until smooth. Add the baking soda, vanilla, salt, raw cacao and chocolate chips and mix well.

Roll 2 tablespoons at a time into round balls. Place on a silpat-lined baking sheet. Use a fork to press the cookies slightly. Bake 10 minutes. Remove from the oven and cool 5-10 minutes on a rack.

Ginger Snaps

Ingredients

- ⅔ cup coconut flour
- 6 tablespoons Great Lakes green label collagen
- ⅔ cup raw unsalted almond butter
- ¼ cup lo han maple syrup
- ¼ cup yacon syrup
- 2 pastured eggs
- 1 teaspoon baking soda
- Pinch of sea salt
- 1 teaspoon vanilla extract
- 1 teaspoon pumpkin spice
- 1 teaspoon ginger

Directions

Preheat oven to 350°F.

Mix the coconut flour, collagen, almond butter, lo han syrup, and yacon syrup in a bowl. Add eggs and beat until smooth. Add the baking soda, vanilla, salt, and spices and mix well.

Roll 2 tablespoons at a time into round balls. Place on a silpat-lined baking sheet. Use a fork to press the cookies slightly. Bake for 10 minutes. Remove from the oven and cool 5-10 minutes on a rack.

Master Recipe for Brownies

Brownies are incredibly versatile and easy to make. This template offers a variety of options for making them to suit the needs of your body and taste.

Directions

Preheat oven to 350°F.

Combine all dry ingredients and set aside.

In a medium saucepan, melt the 3 ounces Lily's chocolate chips over low heat, stirring constantly. Add the almond butter and stir until smooth. Remove from heat and add the coconut oil, lo han syrup, and vanilla. Beat in the eggs until the batter is smooth.

Fold in the dry ingredients. Fold in the additional chocolate chips and pour into a parchment-paper-lined 8 x 8-inch baking pan. Bake 20-25 minutes or until set in the center. Allow to cool completely in the fridge before cutting. These freeze well, so make it a double!

Food Categories	Ingredients	Make it Your Own
"Flour"	½ cup almond flour	Or another nut flour
Binder	2 pastured eggs whisked	One tablespoon flax seeds and three tablespoons of water to replace one egg
Fat	¼ cup melted coconut oil ⅓ cup almond butter	¼ cup melted ghee and ⅓ cup of your favorite nut or seed butter.
Sweetener	⅔ cup lo han "maple" syrup	Or use ⅔ cup coconut sugar, coconut nectar, or 2 mashed bananas or 1 mashed sweet potato
Chocolate	⅓ cup raw cacao powder plus 3 ounces Lily's chocolate chips melted	Make it a double chunk treat by adding another ⅓ cup un-melted Lily's chocolate chips to the batter at the end of your mixing
Flavoring	1 teaspoon vanilla	Make it minty by adding some mint extract or essential oil
Spices	¼ teaspoon sea salt	Pick it up with a little ground ginger and cinnamon or even a pinch of chili powder

Food Categories	Ingredients	Make it Your Own
Other	½ teaspoon baking soda	
Add-ins	Chopped nuts	Drizzle the top with 1 teaspoon coconut oil melted with ⅓ cup Lily's chocolate chips

Triple Chocolate Brownies

Ingredients

½ cup almond flour

¼ cup melted coconut oil

⅓ cup almond butter

⅔ cup lo han maple syurp

⅓ cup raw cocao

3 oz Lilys chocolate chips + 3 oz for folding into the batter

1 teaspoon vanilla

¼ teaspoon sea salt

½ teaspoon baking soda

Reserve a few chocolate chips to be sprinkled on top if desired

Directions

Preheat oven to 350°F.

Combine all dry ingredients and set aside. In a medium saucepan, melt the 3 ounces Lily's chocolate chips over low heat, stirring constantly. Add the almond butter and stir until smooth. Remove from heat and add the coconut oil, lo han syrup, and vanilla. Beat in the eggs until the batter is smooth.

Fold in the dry ingredients. Fold in the additional chocolate chips and pour into a parchment-paper-lined 8 x 8-inch baking pan. Bake 20-25 minutes or until set in the center. Allow to cool completely in the fridge before cutting. Garnish with fresh berries and additional chocolate chips if desired.

Master Recipe for Chocolate Mousse

Mousse is traditionally made with dairy and sugar. However, there are several ways of making it without dairy or sugar that are even better tasting than the original version. Not only that, but this mousse provides healthy fats to balance hormones, regulate the immune system, and create satiety for appetite control and alleviate sugar cravings.

Directions

Peel and pit the avocados if you are using them as the base. If you are using coconut milk for the base, chill the can to separate the cream from the water. If you are using cashews and dates as the base, soak them overnight and pour off the water before proceeding.

Put all ingredients in a high-powered blender or food processer and blend until smooth. Use a rubber spatula to spoon the mixture into individual glass dishes and chill until serving. Garnish with fresh berries and mint leaves, shaved dark chocolate, sifted raw cacao powder and cinnamon, chopped nuts or seeds, toasted coconut flakes, or whipped coconut cream as desired.

Food Categories	Ingredients	Make it Your Own
Base	3 ripe avocados	Or use the cream from the top of a chilled can of full-fat coconut milk plus 3 tablespoons coconut oil Or use 1 cup of raw cashews + 8 pitted dates (soak overnight) and ¼ cup coconut oil with the rest of the recipe
Sweetener	Liquid stevia to taste	You can also use ¼ cup coconut nectar, lo han "maple syrup," or up to 16 pitted dates.
Protein (optional)	8 tablespoons Great Lakes green label collagen	
Liquid	½ cup full-fat coconut milk	

Food Categories	Ingredients	Make it Your Own
Other	½ cup raw cacao	Finely chopped pistachios or other nuts ½ cup tart cherries or other berries ⅓ cup raw cacao nibs Espresso powder Unsweetened coconut flakes
Spice and flavorings	1-2 teaspoons vanilla extract Pinch of sea salt	Nutmeg, ground cloves, ground ginger, ground cinnamon, ancho chili pepper to taste

Mexican Chocolate Mousse

Ingredients
3 ripe avocados
Liquid stevia to taste
8 tablespoons Great Lakes green label collagen
½ cup raw cacao
2 teaspoons vanilla extract
1 teaspoon ancho chili powder
Pinch of sea salt
3 tablespoons full fat coconut cream to be used as a thinner if needed

Directions
Peel and pit the avocados. Put all ingredients in a high-powered blender or food processer and blend until smooth. Thin with full fat coconut milk if needed. Use a rubber spatula to spoon the mixture into individual glass dishes and chill until serving. Garnish with fresh berries and mint leaves, shaved dark chocolate, sifted raw cacao powder and cinnamon, chopped nuts or seeds, toasted coconut flakes, or whipped coconut cream as desired.

Master Recipe for Frozen Desserts

Ice cream with the famous Ewers hot fudge topping has been a favorite for generations in my family. Once again, I thought I was going to live the rest of my life without ice cream after I reversed my autoimmune disease. When I figured out how to make a frozen alternative that was sugar- and dairy-free, I was a very happy woman.

Directions

Combine all ingredients except the ice in a high-powered blender and blend until smooth. Begin adding the ice and blend until desired consistency is reached. Pour into dishes and serve immediately with your favorite toppings.

You can also pour this mixture, minus the ice, into popsicle molds and make ice cream pops for the kids.

Food Categories	Ingredients	Make it Your Own
Base	14-ounce can of full-fat coconut milk	Make your own at home
Sweetener	1-2 tablespoons lo han "maple" syrup	1-2 tablespoons coconut nectar
Fat	¼ cup coconut oil	1 avocado or ¼ cup ghee
Add-ins (mix and match to taste)	½ cup frozen or fresh fruit 2 tablespoons lime juice Handful of minced mint leaves	1-2 tablespoons raw cacao powder 3 tablespoons edible lavender flowers ¾ cup pumpkin puree Cacao nibs or Lily's chocolate chips 1-2 drops essential oils Chopped nuts Fresh herbs
Spice	1 teaspoon vanilla ¼ teaspoon sea salt	Cinnamon, ground ginger, chili pepper, cardamom, allspice
Ice	4 cups	Less if you want it thinner
Protein (optional)	3 tablespoons Great Lakes green label collagen	1 scoop Functional Nutrients Pure and Paleo protein powder

Strawberry Mint "Ice Cream"

Ingredients

1 13½ ounce can of full-fat
  coconut milk
2 tablespoons lo han "maple" syrup
¼ cup coconut oil
½ cup fresh organic strawberries
  finely diced
2 tablespoons lime juice
1 teaspoon vanilla
¼ teaspoon sea salt
2 drops edible mint essential oil or 12
  leaves of fresh mint finely diced
3 tablespoons Great Lakes green
  label collagen
4 cups of ice

Directions

Combine all ingredients except the ice in a high-powered blender and blend until smooth. Begin adding the ice and blend until desired consistency is reached. Pour into dishes and serve immediately with your favorite toppings.

Strawberry Mint "Ice Cream"

Master Recipe for Pudding

Chia pudding is a recipe I give out to my patients who are detoxing. It makes a wonderful quick and easy "clean" dessert. You can make it in a variety of ways to suit your taste and needs.

Directions

Combine all ingredients in a high-powered blender and blend until smooth. Pour into individual serving bowls and refrigerate until firm. Serve chilled with your favorite toppings.

Food Categories	Ingredients	Make it Your Own
Base	14-ounce can of full-fat coconut milk	2 cups of your favorite nut or seed milk
Seeds	½ cup ground flax seeds or chia seeds	½ cup hemp hearts or ground seeds of your choice
Sweetener	1 tablespoon lo han "maple" syrup	1 tablespoon coconut nectar or stevia to taste
Protein (optional)	3 tablespoons Great Lakes green label collagen	1 scoop Functional Nutrients Pure and Paleo Protein Powder
Flavorings	¼-½ teaspoon fresh ginger root grated ½ teaspoon ground cinnamon Pinch of sea salt ¼ teaspoon vanilla	Edible essential oils, cacao nibs, maca powder, other spices or flavorings
Toppings (optional)	½ cup organic berries	Fruit increases sugar content Fresh herb leaves of mint or basil Grated citrus peel Lemon or lime juice ½ cup pumpkin or sweet potato puree 2 tablespoons raw cacao powder Chopped nuts or seeds Lily's chocolate chips

Detox Friendly Chia Pudding

Ingredients
1 13½ ounce can of full-fat
    coconut milk
½ cup white chia seeds
1 tablespoon lo han "maple" syrup
3 tablespoons Great Lakes green
    label collagen
½ teaspoon fresh ginger root grated
½ teaspoon ground cinnamon
Pinch of sea salt
¼ teaspoon vanilla
½ cup organic blue berries

Directions
Combine all ingredients in a high-powered blender and blend until smooth. Pour into individual serving bowls and refrigerate until firm. Serve chilled with your favorite toppings.

Master Recipe for Crust-less Pies

The part of baking a pie that is time consuming and not particularly healthy is the crust. One day I was contemplating this fact and realized I enjoy the filling of a pie much more than I do the crust, so why not just make the pie without a crust? I made a sweet potato pie and it was delicious AND super easy and fast to make. Win-win.

Directions
Bake, peel, and mash the cooled sweet potatoes. Combine the mashed potatoes with the rest of the ingredients (except the pecans) in a high-powered blender and blend until smooth. Pour into one large deep-dish pie plate or several small individual-sized pie plates or even muffin cups. Bake in a 350°F oven until set. It will take 40 minutes for the mini-pie size to bake all the way through. Allow to sit for 10 minutes before serving. Serve with whipped coconut cream if desired (see directions below).

Food Categories	Ingredients	Make it Your Own
Protein	6 tablespoons Great Lakes green label collagen (optional)	
Base	6 cups baked, peeled, and mashed sweet potatoes (6 medium sweet potatoes baked for 1 hour in a 350°F oven	Or use 6 cups pumpkin puree, roasted butternut squash, or roasted acorn squash
Sweetener	⅔ cup lo han "maple" syrup	Or use ½ cup coconut nectar or yacon syrup
Binder	6 pastured eggs whisked	One tablespoon flax seeds and three tablespoons of water to replace one egg
Spice	2 teaspoons vanilla 1 tablespoon pumpkin pie spice Pinch of sea salt	Other spices or flavorings
Topping (optional)	Pecan halves to garnish the top Whipped coconut cream	Other nuts

Easy Crust-less Pumpkin Pie

Ingredients

    6 tablespoons Great Lakes green
        label collagen
    2 cups pumpkin puree
    2/3 cup yacon syrup
    6 pastured eggs
    2 teaspoon vanilla
    1 tablespoon pumpkin pie spice
    Pinch of sea salt

Directions

Combine the pumpkin puree with the yacon syrup, eggs, vanilla, spice and sea salt in a high-powered blender and blend until smooth. Pour into one large deep-dish pie plate or several small individual-sized pie plates or even muffin cups. Bake in a 350°F oven until set. It will take 40 minutes for the mini-pie size to bake all the way through. Allow to sit for 10 minutes before serving.

Easy Crust-less Pumpkin Pie

Want to make your pie with a pie crust? Here's a delicious recipe for a paleo pie crust you can make for any pie of your choosing.

Paleo Pie Crust

Ingredients
1 cup blanched and sifted almond flour (not almond meal)
½ cup coconut flour
½ cup tapioca or arrowroot flour
½ teaspoon sea salt
½ cup palm shortening that has been refrigerated for 1 hour
2 large pastured eggs
1 teaspoon almond milk

Directions
Sift the almond flour, coconut flour, tapioca flour and salt together until well combined. Add the cold palm shortening to the flour by cutting it into the flour with 2 knives, using a pastry cutter, or with a food processor until the dough looks like small peas. Add one of the eggs and mix only until the dough begins to form.

Roll the dough out to a flattened oval, cover with plastic wrap and chill in fridge for 30 minutes.

Lightly flour a sheet of parchment paper with tapioca flour or arrowroot flour. Take the dough out of the fridge and place on the parchment paper.

Lightly sprinkle the top of the dough with more tapioca or arrowroot flour and cover with another sheet of parchment paper. Roll with a rolling pin until the dough is 12 inches in diameter and ⅛ inch thick. Alternatively, you can press the dough with your fingers directly into the pie plate if your dough is too crumbly. Don't let the dough stick to the paper. Use more flour as needed.

Carefully move the dough from the parchment paper to your pie dish, repairing any cracks as you go.

Crimp the edges. Separate the second egg, saving the egg white. Whisk the egg white with 1 teaspoon of water or almond milk to make an egg wash.

Brush the egg wash onto the edges of the pie dish onto the dough. If you have dough left over, you can decorate the top of your pie with fancy cutouts and designs. Use the egg wash on those to help them adhere to the top of the pie and to give them a pretty sheen.

For an unfilled pie crust: preheat the oven to 375°F. Bake for 15 minutes or until the edges just turn golden. Allow to cool on a wire rack before filling.

For a double-crust pie:

Double the recipe and divide the dough into two equal sections. Proceed as above. Bake according to the directions of the pie filling you are making.

Easy Coconut Whipped Cream

Ingredients

1 can of full fat coconut milk
1 tablespoon maple syrup or Lo Han maple syrup
1 teaspoon homemade vanilla extract
pinch of sea salt

Directions

Place the can of coconut milk in the refrigerator overnight. Chill a glass or metal bowl in the freezer along with your beaters for at least 30 minutes. Remove the coconut milk from the fridge and open carefully so you don't disturb the separation. Scoop off the cream that has risen to the top and place in the chilled bowl. Add the syrup, salt, and vanilla and beat until smooth. Serve immediately.

Easy Coconut
Whipped Cream

Master Recipe for Cake

Birthdays are usually celebrated with either cake or cupcakes. This is my favorite cake recipe. You can alter it in a variety of ways to suit the needs of the occasion. This is the answer for my patients who tell me they have "fallen off of the wagon" because of a birthday or holiday celebration. Now there's no need to go off of your food plan for any reason.

Directions

Preheat oven to 350°F.

Prepare the bottom and sides of a 7-inch springform pan by greasing with ghee or coconut oil and line the bottom with a round of parchment paper cut to fit the pan.

In a food processor, pulse the almond flour, coconut flour, raw cacao powder (if you are baking a chocolate cake), sweetener of your choice, baking soda, sea salt, and whatever dried spices you are using.

In your high-powered blender, blend the melted fat of your choice, liquid, eggs, and vanilla.

Fold the dry ingredients into the wet ingredients to make a smooth batter but don't over mix it.

Pour the batter into your greased pan and bake until a toothpick inserted into the center comes out clean, approximately 45-50 minutes.

Let the cake cool completely before frosting with one of the following frosting variations. For a fancier cake, you can add a ganache filling between two layers of cake. If you choose to do this, you will need to carefully cut your cake horizontally through the middle to create 2 layers. Using a rubber spatula, swirl the ganache onto the bottom layer and then chill in the fridge for 20-30 minutes. Add the top layer and frost the entire cake using a variation from the following frosting recipe template. Garnish the top with mint leaves and fresh berries, toasted coconut flakes, nuts, shaved chocolate or edible flowers as desired.

Ganache Recipe

Ingredients

1 can (13½ ounces) full-fat coconut milk
¼ cup lo han "maple syrup"
1 teaspoon vanilla bean powder
1 teaspoon sea salt
For chocolate ganache: ¼ cup raw cacao powder
For German Chocolate filling: 1 cup unsweetened coconut flakes and ½ cup chopped pecans

Directions

On the stovetop, heat the coconut milk and sweetener until it just comes to a boil. Stir to prevent from burning. Turn the heat down and simmer for 1 to 2 hours, stirring periodically to prevent it from burning. When the coconut milk has thickened and the liquid is half of where it started, it is done. Add the vanilla and a pinch of sea salt and you have a rich caramel ganache. If you want to make a praline filling, you can add 1 cup unsweetened coconut flakes and ½ cup finely chopped pecans. If you want to make it chocolate, you can add the cacao powder and mix until smooth. Store in your refrigerator until you are ready to apply to the bottom layer of the cake.

Food Categories	Ingredients	Make it Your Own
"Flour"	3 cups blanched almond flour ¼ cup coconut flour	Honeyville almond flour works the best to keep the cake light and from sinking in the middle.
Sweetener	½ cup granulated monk fruit	½ cup coconut palm sugar or yacon syrup (has a molasses taste if you want a gingerbread taste)
Liquid	1 cup full fat coconut milk	1 cup any seed or nut milk
Binder	3 large pastured eggs	One tablespoon flax seeds and three tablespoons of water to replace one egg
Fat	½ cup melted coconut oil	½ cup melted ghee or creamy nut or seed butter
Other	2 teaspoons baking soda	
Spice and flavorings	2 teaspoons vanilla bean powder 1 teaspoon sea salt ¾ cup raw cacao powder (for a chocolate cake)	Use ½ cup Lily's stevia chocolate chips for more chocolate power or just to make a nut-butter-chocolate-chip yellow cake. You can add cinnamon, ground ginger, chili pepper, cardamom, or allspice to perk up the spiciness. For a red velvet cake, add some dried beet powder to get the red color.

Master Recipe for Frostings

Directions

Refrigerate the can of coconut milk for 2 hours or overnight to get the cream to rise to the surface.

When the coconut milk is chilled, open the can and carefully remove the solid cream from the top, discarding the water.

In a chilled metal mixing bowl, whip the cream, vanilla, stevia, and salt until they are fluffy.

Make it your own by using the variations provided in the chart.

Use on cakes or cupcakes. Tastes great with fruit too. Stores in the fridge up to 3 days in an air-tight container.

Food Categories	Ingredients	Make it Your Own
Base	1 can (13½ ounces) full-fat coconut milk	You can also use ¼ cup powdered coconut sugar (pulse it in blender to powder it), or powdered monk fruit.
Sweetener	4-6 drops liquid stevia	
Fat		¼ cup coconut oil chilled in fridge, mixed with 1 cup melted Lily's chocolate chips; the vanilla and salt make a lovely chocolate frosting.
Other		Add ¼ cup pureed pumpkin with the spices below to the base recipe, and you get a creamy pumpkin frosting that tastes great on chocolate or gingerbread cakes.
Spice and flavorings	1-2 teaspoons vanilla extract Pinch of sea salt	Nutmeg, ground cloves, ground ginger, ground cinnamon, chili pepper to taste 3 tablespoons raw cacao

Dreamy Chocolate Cake

Ingredients for cake base
Almond flour
Coconut flour
Baking soda
Cocoa powder
Eggs
Coconut milk
Coconut palm sugar
Coconut oil
Vanilla
Salt

Directions
Preheat oven to 350°F.

Prepare the bottom and sides of a 7-inch springform pan by greasing with ghee or coconut oil and line the bottom with a round of parchment paper cut to fit the pan.

In a food processor, pulse the almond flour, coconut flour, raw cacao powder, coconut palm sugar, baking soda, sea salt, and vanilla.

In your high-powered blender, blend the coconut oil, coconut milk, eggs, and vanilla.

Fold the dry ingredients into the wet ingredients to make a smooth batter but don't over mix it. Pour the batter into your greased pan and bake until a toothpick inserted into the center comes out clean, approximately 45-50 minutes.

Let the cake cool completely on a cooling rack. When completely cool slice the cake horizontally all the way through with a long knife to create 2 layers. Spread the ganache filling on the bottom layer and then chill in the fridge for 20-30 minutes. Add the top layer and frost the entire cake; top and sides. Garnish the top with mint leaves and fresh berries.

Coconut Pecan Ganache

Ingredients for cake base
1 13½ ounce can full-fat
   coconut milk
¼ cup lo han "maple syrup"
1 teaspoon vanilla bean powder or
   vanilla extract
1 teaspoon sea salt
1 cup unsweetened coconut flakes
½ cup chopped pecans

Directions
On the stovetop, heat the coconut milk and lo han syrup until it just comes to a boil. Stir to prevent from burning. Turn the heat down and simmer for 1-2 hours, stirring periodically to prevent it from burning. When the coconut milk has thickened and the liquid is half of where it started, it is done. Add the vanilla, flaked coconut, chopped pecans, and a pinch of sea salt. Spread over the bottom layer of the cake and then top with the second layer, getting it ready to frost.

Chocolate Fudge Frosting

Ingredients for cake base
1 13½ oz can of coconut milk
4 drops liquid stevia
3 tablespoons raw cacao powder

Directions

Refrigerate the can of coconut milk for 2 hours or overnight to get the cream to rise to the surface.

When the coconut milk is chilled, open the can and carefully remove the solid cream from the top, discarding the water. In a chilled metal mixing bowl, whip the cream, vanilla, stevia, cacao powder and salt until they are fluffy. Frost the top and sides of the layered cake.

Afterword

There are many "reasons" I hear in my practice from people about why it's not possible for them to eat in a way that truly nourishes their whole being. I encourage you to live an unreasonable life. Every time you come up with a reason to be out of integrity with your body, mind, and spirit, move against it. If it's because it's your birthday, or you're traveling, or it's a holiday, just choose one of the delicious and easy-to-make recipes from this book and stay in integrity.

Food is eaten for many reasons besides hunger. Those reasons range from celebrations to boredom; from stimulating your energy to calming your emotions; from reward to punishment. Yet just as it's not possible to find happiness in sex, money, or drugs, it's also not possible to find happiness in food. I want to share a story I learned several years ago from one of my teachers, Ramana Maharshi.

Once there was a woman who had a precious necklace that she wore around her neck. One day when she was distracted, she forgot the necklace and believed it to be lost. The woman frantically searched her home, garden, and surrounding neighborhood but could not find it. She asked her friends and neighbors if they knew anything about the necklace. They did not. At last a friend asked her to look under her blouse, just in case she had it on but had forgotten she put it on. Sure enough, there it was. She had been wearing it all along. She was both elated and relieved her precious necklace was not lost. When others asked her later if she had found the necklace that was lost, she said, "Yes, thank you, I found it." And each time she felt a wave of happiness that the necklace had not been lost.

Notice the fluctuation of feelings this woman experienced. She went from contented to panic stricken and anxious to elated and overjoyed. Her happiness was because she thought she had recovered a lost treasure. Similarly, we imagine that we will be happy at some point in time; when we have met our weight goal, have earned a certain amount of money, have met our soulmate, have the job we have always dreamt of, when we aren't so busy. However, the feeling we imagine we will have when we meet those goals is within us at all times. There is nothing outside of you that will fill any perceived lack you believe you have; that includes food. Just like the necklace, happiness and wholeness is with you at all times, even when you think you have lost or misplaced it.

May you live the rest of your days with the knowledge that you are whole and complete just as you are. May you reach for food only when you are hungry, and may that food always nourish and strengthen you so that you reach your potential and live the mission you are here to live, in the service of all you share this planet with. May you share the knowledge you have learned here with others who also need to reduce their inflammation and reverse their chronic illnesses. In this way we will reverse the autoimmune disease that threatens our society; by healing yourself and expanding your own consciousness and then showing the way to another.

Much love and many blessings,
Dr. Keesha Ewers
San Juan Island, WA
May 2018

About the Author

Dr. Keesha Ewers is an integrative medicine expert, a Doctor of Sexology, a Psychotherapist, board certified in Functional medicine, holds an advanced certification in Ayurvedic medicine, and is the founder and medical director of the Academy for Integrative Medicine.

Dr. Keesha has been in the medical field for over 30 years. After being diagnosed with rheumatoid arthritis—an incurable disease according to Western medicine—she discovered how to reverse autoimmunity using her Freedom Framework® Method. She has now successfully used this same method with thousands of her own patients and teaches it to her health coach students.

As the Mystic Medicine™ Doctor, her constant thirst for knowledge in the pursuit of finding answers to human suffering has taken her around the world, learning from traditional healers and native cultures from Australia to Peru, from India to Africa. She has also studied the best of the innovative thinkers, mystics, and scientists the West has to offer.

Dr. Keesha is a popular speaker, including from the TEDx stage, and the best-selling author of *Solving the Autoimmune Puzzle: The Woman's Guide to Reclaiming Emotional Freedom and Vibrant Health* and *Your Libido Story: A workbook for women who want to find, fix, and free*

their sexual desire. She is also the founder of a branch of medicine now called Functional Sexology®.

In her free time, Dr. Keesha is likely found trying out new recipes in her kitchen on San Juan Island, traipsing the mountains, hills, and beaches of the Pacific Northwest, or kayaking with her husband and three golden doodles.

Go to DrKeesha.com to listen to Dr. Keesha's Mystic Medicine Radio Show, find her books and programs, join her next Mystic Medicine Deep Immersion Retreat, apply to become a patient, or enroll in her health coach certification program.

Made in the USA
Columbia, SC
09 April 2023

14668837R00139